Build the Non-Contact Voltage Detector.

www.radioshack.com/DIT

D.I.T. ®radioshack

PARTS

- ○ Dual Mini Perfboard 276-148
- ○ 2N3904 Transistor (3) 276-2016
- ○ 1/4W Resistors (1M, 100K and 220)
- ○ Hookup Wire 278-1224
- ○ 5mm Red LED 276-041
- ○ Heat-Shrink Tubing 278-1627
- ○ Momentary Pushbutton Switch 275-1556
- ○ 9V Snap Connector 270-324
- ○ 9V Battery 23-2209
- ○ Project Enclosure 270-1801
- ○ LED Holder 276-079
- ○ Copper-Clad PC Board 276-1499
- ○ Double-Sided Foam Tape 640-2343

TOOLS

- ○ Soldering Iron and Solder 64-053, 64-013
- ○ Wire Cutter 64-064
- ○ Pliers 64-062
- ○ Wire Stripper 64-224
- ○ Drill and Drill Bits
- ○ Rotary Tool and Saw Blade 64-149

4

Drill a 5/16" hole in the top right of the enclosure lid, just below the lid's screw hole. Drill a 1/4" hole in the top left, also below the lid's screw hole. Insert the LED holder into the 1/4" hole from the outside and the LED into the holder from the inside. Remove the plastic button, mount the switch body into the 5/16" hole with its bundled hardware, tighten down and reattach the button.

5

Cut a 3/4" × 1-1/2" strip of copper-clad board with a rotary tool and stick it to one end of the enclosure with double-sided tape. Drill a 1/16" hole through both copper and case near the middle of the strip. Thread the green wire from the perfboard through the hole from inside, bend it over and solder it to the copper.

6

Clip a battery to the connector and insert it, along with the perfboard, into the enclosure body. Orient the solder side of the perfboard toward the battery. Route any excess wire and gently close the lid. Screw it in place.

7

Hold the detector near an appliance cord and press the button; the LED will glow if the cord is live. The device can also be used to detect static charge. Got a feline friend nearby? Try testing the detector against its fur. Now go experiment and have fun! (But stay clear of any bare wires that might carry dangerous currents!)

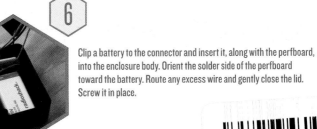

D0817424

®radioshack

CONTENTS

COLUMNS

ON THE COVER:
Emily Pilloton of Project H on location in the blacksmithing room at the Crucible in Oakland.

FEATURES

CONTENTS

SKILL BUILDERS

86

82

92

74

64

PROJECTS

TOOLBOX

Vol. 40, July 2014. Make: (ISSN 1556-2336) is published bimonthly by Maker Media, Inc. in the months of January, March, May, July, September, and November. Maker Media is located at 1005 Gravenstein Hwy. North, Sebastopol, CA 95472, (707) 827-7000. SUBSCRIPTIONS: Send all subscription requests to Make:, P.O. Box 17046, North Hollywood, CA 91615-9588 or subscribe online at makezine.com/offer or via phone at (866) 289-8847 (U.S. and Canada); all other countries call (818) 487-2037. Subscriptions are available for $34.95 for 1 year (6 issues) in the United States; in Canada: $39.95 USD; all other countries: $49.95 USD. Periodicals Postage Paid at Sebastopol, CA, and at additional mailing offices. POSTMASTER: Send address changes to Make:, P.O. Box 17046, North Hollywood, CA 91615-9588. Canada Post Publications Mail Agreement Number 41129568. CANADA POSTMASTER: Send address changes to: Maker Media, PO Box 456, Niagara Falls, ON L2E 6V2

Get the *Make:* iPad App!

A totally new way to experience Make!

Take *Make:* to the Next Level

- Interactive Content
- Video Integration with Tutorials
- Expanded Project Builds

Make:

Find out more at: makezine.com/go/ipadapp

FOUNDER & CEO
Dale Dougherty
dale@makezine.com

CFO
Todd Sotkiewicz
todd@makezine.com

> "The 3D printer gets 'em in the door, but the laser cutter keeps 'em coming back."
> —*Anonymous*

EDITOR-IN-CHIEF
Mark Frauenfelder
markf@makezine.com

EDITORIAL

EXECUTIVE EDITOR
Mike Senese
msenese@makezine.com

COMMUNITY EDITOR
Caleb Kraft
caleb@makermedia.com

MANAGING EDITOR
Cindy Lum

PROJECTS EDITOR
Keith Hammond
khammond@makezine.com

SENIOR EDITOR
Goli Mohammadi

TECHNICAL EDITORS
Sean Michael Ragan
David Scheltema

DIGITAL FABRICATION EDITOR
Anna Kaziunas France

EDITORS
Laura Cochrane
Nathan Hurst

EDITORIAL ASSISTANT
Craig Couden

COPY EDITOR
Laurie Barton

PUBLISHER, BOOKS
Brian Jepson

EDITOR, BOOKS
Patrick DiJusto

CONTRIBUTING EDITORS
William Gurstelle, Nick Normal,
Charles Platt, Matt Richardson

CONTRIBUTING WRITERS
John Baichtal, Matt Bates,
Robert Beatty, Phil Bowie, Eric
Chu, Robert Cook, Larry Cotton,
DC Denison, Stuart Deutsch,
Tony DiCola, Tomas Diez, Lendy
Dunaway, James Floyd Kelly,
Andy Forest, Neil Gershenfeld,
Travis Good, Vicente Guallart,
Georgia Guthrie, Gregory
Hayes, Jack Hegenauer, Ross
Hershberger, Stett Holbrook
William Holman, John Iovine,
Fredrik Jansson, Matt Keeter,
Stuart Kestenbaum, Bob
Knetzger, Victor Konshin,
Sherry Lassiter, Marco Mahler,
Samantha Matalone Cook,
Forrest M. Mims III, Dug North,
Ronald Pattinson, Nadya Peek,
David Perry, Paul Rawlinson,
Molly Rubenstein, Rick Schertle,
Omar-Pierre Soubra, Dirk Swart,
Jennifer Turliuk, Shawn Wallace,
Eric Weinhoffer, Kyle Wiens, Tyler
Winegarner, Tyler Worman

CREATIVE DIRECTOR
Jason Babler
jbabler@makezine.com

**DESIGN,
PHOTOGRAPHY
& VIDEO**

ART DIRECTOR
Juliann Brown

SENIOR DESIGNER
Pete Ivey

DESIGNER
Jim Burke

PHOTO EDITOR
Jeffrey Braverman

PHOTOGRAPHER
Gunther Kirsch

MULTIMEDIA PRODUCER
Emmanuel Mota

VIDEOGRAPHER
**Nat Wilson-
Heckathorn**

FABRICATOR
Daniel Spangler

WEBSITE

MANAGING DIRECTOR
Alice Hill

WEB DEVELOPER
Jake Spurlock

WEB PRODUCERS
Bill Olson
David Beauchamp

CONTRIBUTING ARTISTS
Matthew Billington, Bob
Knetzger, Shannon Murphy, Rob
Nance, Damien Scogin, Julie
West, Jing Zhang

ONLINE CONTRIBUTORS
Alasdair Allan, Jimmy DiResta,
Agnes Niewiadomski, Haley
Pierson-Cox, Andrew Salomone,
Andrew Terranova

ENGINEERING INTERNS
Paloma Fautley, Sam Freeman,
Andrew Katz (jr.), Brian Melani,
Nick Parks, Sam Scheiner,
Wynter Woods

Comments may be sent to:
editor@makezine.com

Visit us online:
makezine.com

Follow us on Twitter:
@make @makerfaire
@craft @makershed

On Google+:
google.com/+make

On Facebook:
makemagazine

VICE PRESIDENT
Sherry Huss
sherry@makezine.com

**SALES
& ADVERTISING**

SENIOR SALES
MANAGER
Katie D. Kunde
katie@makezine.com

SALES MANAGERS
Cecily Benzon
cbenzon@makezine.com
Brigitte Kunde
brigitte@makezine.com

CLIENT SERVICES
MANAGERS
Mara Lincoln
Miranda Mager

MARKETING
COORDINATOR
Karlee Vincent

COMMERCE

DIRECTOR OF
SHED DESIGN
Riley Wilkinson

OPERATIONS MANAGER
Rob Bullington

SENIOR CHANNEL
MANAGER
Ilana Budanitsky

PRODUCT INNOVATION
MANAGER
Michael Castor

MARKETING

VICE PRESIDENT OF
MARKETING
Vickie Welch
vwelch@makezine.com

MARKETING PROGRAMS
MANAGER
Suzanne Huston

MARKETING SERVICES
COORDINATOR
Johanna Nuding

DIRECTOR, RETAIL
MARKETING &
OPERATIONS
**Heather Harmon
Cochran**
heatherh@makezine.com

MAKER FAIRE

PRODUCER
Louise Glasgow

PROGRAM DIRECTOR
Sabrina Merlo

MARKETING & PR
**Bridgette
Vanderlaan**

**CUSTOM
PROGRAMS**

DIRECTOR
Michelle Hlubinka

**CUSTOMER
SERVICE**

CUSTOMER CARE
TEAM LEADER
Daniel Randolph
cs@readerservices.
makezine.com

Manage your account
online, including change
of address:
makezine.com/account
866-289-8847 toll-free
in U.S. and Canada
818-487-2037,
5 a.m.–5 p.m., PST
makezine.com

PUBLISHED BY

MAKER MEDIA, INC.
Dale Dougherty, CEO

Copyright © 2014
Maker Media, Inc.
All rights reserved.
Reproduction without
permission is prohibited.
Printed in the USA by
Schumann Printers, Inc.

CONTRIBUTORS

What skill would you like to learn?

Jing Zhang
London, United Kingdom
(Geek Club illustration)

I would love to learn painting properly. I learned some basics of painting when I was a kid, which is why I later developed as an illustrator. Going back to traditional artist is definitely something I'd love to achieve in my life.

Georgia Guthrie
Philadelphia, Pennsylvania
(Where Are the Women?)

I would like to take a deeper dive into programming with processing. I used it a few years ago to do some experimentation with facial tracking in my grad program, but I know it's changed a lot since then.

Ronald Pattinson
Amsterdam, The Netherlands
(Brew a Vintage IPA)

Learning to video edit is a skill I would love to learn. With my children approaching adulthood, I won't be able to bribe them into nailing together the scraps of video I take into something vaguely watchable for much longer.

Tony DiCola
Kirkland, Washington
(Face Recognition Treasure Safe)

I'd like to learn about 3D printing and CAD so I can build custom project cases, design prototypes, and even print spare parts to fix broken things.

David Perry
Portland, Oregon
(3D-Printed Electric Violin)

One of my upcoming projects combines 3D printing, microcontrollers, and textiles, so I need to brush up on my programming and electronics skills, but I'm really excited to learn to sew from scratch! I love working with my hands, and my most fun ideas come while I'm learning new things.

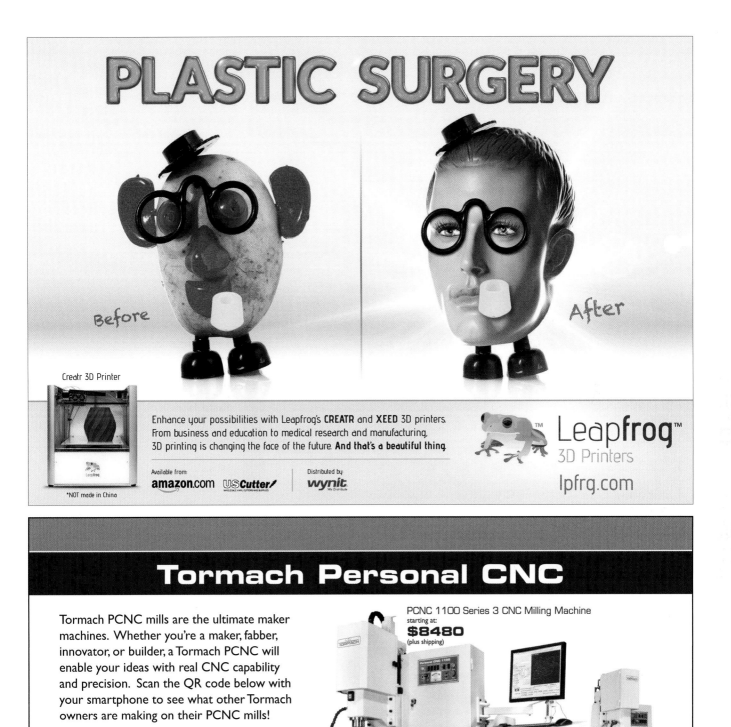

BY DALE
DOUGHERTY,
founder and CEO of
Maker Media.

Makerspaces Are Working Out

"IT'S LIKE A GYM WHERE YOU GET A MEMBERSHIP TO USE THE EQUIPMENT."
That was the basic idea for TechShop, as explained to me by founder Jim Newton at our first Maker Faire in April of 2006. He asked me for a table so he could hang his sign, deliver his pitch, and see if people were interested. The fact that he showed up in a vintage military transport vehicle had some bearing on my decision to say yes. The interest proved strong enough for Jim to get backers and open the first TechShop in an industrial park in Menlo Park, California, in October 2006.

Almost from inception, TechShop was a dream — not only Jim's but one shared by its members — to have unlimited access to the tools of a machine shop, plus new tools for digital fabrication such as laser cutters and 3D printers, for a modest monthly fee.

What do people really do at TechShop? There are a group of makers who show up with a pretty clear idea of what they want to do. They have a project to work on. Often it has some practical or commercial application, and they lack a place where they could develop their idea into something real. Others show up and want to belong but don't have a project or purpose. They want to learn how to use the tools, and maybe that will lead

them somewhere. David Lang was one of those people, and he wrote about his experience in the book *Zero to Maker*.

Some have tried to implement what TechShop has done. In Shenzhen, China, I came across TechSpace. Others, while similar to TechShop, are different in that they're locally owned and operated, such as Maker Works in Ann Arbor, Michigan.

Gui Cavalcanti, who started a similar shared workspace in 2004, learned some key lessons from its failure and started thinking of a new model. This became Artisan's Asylum in Somerville, Massachusetts, which now occupies a 24,000-square-foot space that was originally an envelope factory. He had a budget of $40,000 to open the space and outfit it. Most of the tools were used, either donated by members or acquired for the cost of removing them from a former worksite. Artisan's Asylum is most successful at building a community among its members, some of whom rent their own workspace. It has become not just a place to do your own work but a kind of "collaborative commons," to use the phrase from Jeremy Rifkin's book, *The Zero Marginal Cost Society*.

There are also quite a number of hackerspaces, which tend to be like clubs,

almost always run by volunteers. Some are members-only and others are open to the public for free, like Noisebridge in San Francisco. Some hackerspaces are rather like an eccentric's garage full of scavenged treasure and forever awaiting someone to whip it into shape. A hackerspace is as much a meeting place as a workplace.

Artisan's Asylum represents what I might call a middle tier between large-scale TechShops and small-scale hackerspaces, a trend toward the professionalization of makerspaces. That is, they must be able to perform a core set of services to support membership growth. A makerspace needs to greet new members and provide basic safety training as well as offer workshops for members who arrive without project ideas.

Indeed, a gym is a good analogy to understand makerspaces. Today's health clubs started out years ago as bodybuilding gyms. They were designed to meet the needs of a narrow, largely male membership. They weren't particularly friendly to newcomers or casual users. Yet something changed in our culture around physical fitness, and health clubs became more open and accommodating, to broaden membership by welcoming women as well as men, and the serious as well as the casual member. This is what we're seeing as makerspaces transition from volunteer efforts serving a small group of members.

Neil Gershenfeld designed and built Fab Labs, the first of which was opened in Boston in 2004. Gershenfeld's Center for Bits and Atoms might be considered the R&D lab for digital fabrication, with state-of-the-art tools organized in service of an inevitable vision of our technological future. While there are a variety of settings, from science museums to community colleges, Fab Labs are funded and managed in a top-down fashion that's consistent with their academic origins. Independently, a growing number of makerspaces are getting established at universities, such as Yale, Georgia Tech, Case Western Reserve, and SMU. These spaces are designed for students and their projects.

It doesn't much matter what you call them — TechShops, makerspaces, hackerspaces, or Fab Labs. Makers are doing cool stuff, and having access to tools, community, and mentors really does matter. We need more local places for makers to work out new ideas. ●

Jeffrey Braverman

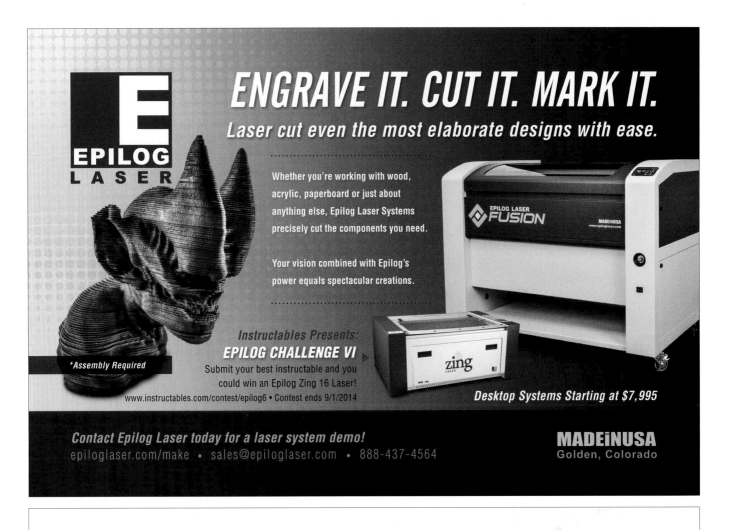

Pirates, Plushies, and Proper Definitions

>> As soon as we saw the Raspberry Pirate Radio project (Volume 38, page 80, makezine.com/projects/raspberry-pirate-radio), we decided to try it. My brother and I had so much fun! Our friends (who are also Raspberry Pi fanatics) came over the next day and were inspired to build one also. They live across the street from an ice rink, and one day when we were skating there, they played their radio station! We heard a few recordings that we made ("This is Schatz Radio, 93.7"), and a fake commercial for the Raspberry Pi that we added. Anyway, I want to thank *Make:* for a great time and an amazing educational experience for us.
— *Nate Schatz, age 13, Kodiak, Alaska*

+ Listen to their audio clips: makezine.com/go/raspirates

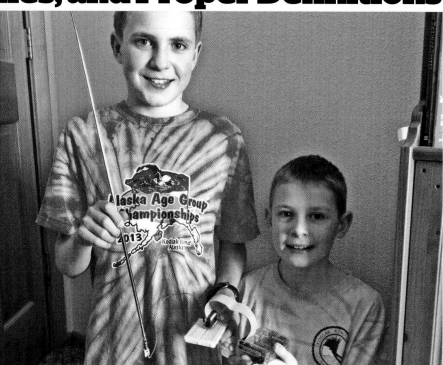

>> I really enjoyed "DIY Video Game Plushies from 3D Models" (Volume 38, page 72, makezine.com/projects/video-game-plushies). It showed a creative use of technology that I had never dreamed of. (Even if I had tried to make a plushy from the texture-map skins of a 3D model, I probably would have approached it using papercraft techniques.) It's a great article except for one thing: It suggests stealing art and even gives detailed instructions on where to find art to steal and tools for stealing it. This is like starting an article on silversmithing by telling the reader what stores are likely to have silver and then giving tips on breaking and entering.

The second article that bothered me was "Kickstart a Kids' Makerspace" (Volume 38, page 28, makezine.com/kids-makerspace). I'm 100% behind the idea of creating makerspaces for kids and teaching the necessary skills; I am a third-generation teacher and my daughter is training to be the fourth. The #1 problem with the article is that it does not state a use case. How many students can use the space at one time? What skills will be taught and demonstrated using the space? How will it fit into an existing curriculum? Another thing that left me deeply troubled was the lack of a budget for safety equipment; for training people to supervise the makerspace; for simple things like tables, chairs, extension cords, lamps, shelves, or locking cabinets; the cost of rooms used to house the makerspace; or consumables, maintenance, or other recurring costs (other than a one-time purchase of 3D printer filament). Remember, there are always at least three ways to do anything — the one that looks obvious, quick, and simple is never one of them.
—*Bob Pendleton, Round Rock, Texas*

**PROJECTS EDITOR
KEITH HAMMOND RESPONDS:**
>> Bob, thanks for reading so closely! In "Video Game Plushies," we didn't tell readers to steal art. We recommended extracting 3D models from a game you own, downloading from authorized sites, or searching repositories online; it's the reader's responsibility to know and follow the law.

"Kickstart a Kids' Makerspace" was focused on choosing and financing high-tech tools, but you're right, our list should have included safety gear to accompany those tools. As for use cases and overhead costs, makerspaces are used in different ways — by classes or clubs; during, after, or completely outside school — and those considerations were beyond the scope of the article. As for housing, you might enjoy our new "CNC Makerspace Shed" project on page 30 of this issue (it comfortably seats 16 at worktables).

MAKE AMENDS:

■ Multiple designs featured in "Open-Source CNC Furniture" (Volume 39, page 74, makezine.com/magazine/open-source-furniture) and "CNC Maker Bench" (Volume 38, page 98, makezine.com/projects/cnc-maker-bench) were erroneously described as "open source." The CC BY-NC-SA license used by these designs places commercial restrictions on their use and violates the sixth provision of the Open Source Definition (Annotated): "No Discrimination Against Fields of Endeavor."

Right to Repair

Fight for your right to truly own your things.

Written by Kyle Wiens ■ Illustration by Jim Burke

IF MY PHONE WERE A PERSON, IT WOULD BE THE BIONIC WOMAN. Its body has been broken and rebuilt more times than I can count. Its brain has been modified, tinkered with, and improved.

In the past three years, my iPhone 4S has been jailbroken and wired into a home automation system. Its Apple-approved glass back panel has been replaced with a transparent one. It's been water-drenched, dismantled, and completely cleaned. Twice. Thanks to an app from the free-as-in-speech Cydia store, I'm tracking my battery's performance in ways Apple won't allow. And I've pried up and replaced that battery over and over again.

It's the phone that will not die — at least not if I have anything to say about it.

Ten years ago, I started iFixit, the world's free online repair manual. Our goal is to teach everyone how to fix the stuff they own — whether it's laptops, snowboards, toys, or clothes. And we're not alone. iFixit is part of a global network of fixers trying to make the stuff we own last forever.

On the surface, fixers and makers are cut from different cloth. Makers put things together; fixers take them apart. One creates new gizmos; the other rebuilds existing ones. But I've always thought that, under the skin, they're incredibly similar — two different sides of the same coin.

We are, all of us, tinkerers. We're motivated by the same ideals: an inexhaustible curiosity, an appreciation for things done by hand, a sentimental attachment to the smell of wood shavings, and a never-ending pursuit of understanding the things around us.

As tinkerers, we become more than just consumers. We are participants in the things we make, own, and fix. But over the years, I have found that this participation — tinkering with products made by others — puts both makers and fixers at

odds with manufacturers. (Apple certainly wouldn't endorse my bionic iPhone.) For the most part, manufacturers would prefer if we all just put down our screw-drivers and got back in line at the store.

By revealing (and reveling in) the secret insides of machines, tinkerers transgress the boundaries of what manufacturers think we should be able to do with our stuff. We alter the code they wrote, we rebuild

the hardware they designed, and we find ways of fixing our old stuff instead of buying their new stuff.

For the past 20 years, manufacturers have been waging a quiet war against tinkerers like us. They're using encryption-powered DRM, vague hand-waving claims of proprietary knowledge, DMCA takedown notices, and legal threats to keep people from fixing their tractors, from repairing their Apple products, and even from modifying the software on their calcula-

tors. Keurig is even adding a chip to their coffee pods to prevent homebrewers from "reloading" their capsules.

It's been more than a year since 114,000 people signed a We the People petition to legalize cellphone unlocking, but switching carriers is still a crime — despite intensive lobbying from digital rights groups including the Electronic Frontier Foundation.

Even the car industry — sacred ground for tinkerers since the rise of the hot rod — has succumbed to the same locked-door policies. These days, cars are made up of as much code as they are nuts and bolts. Tinkering under the hood requires access to service information and schematic systems — information that carmakers don't like to share. In Massachusetts, voters had to pass a law to force automakers to share internal service manuals, circuit diagrams, and computer codes with independent repair shops and owners.

I think that if you bought it, you own it. I mean *really* own it. You have the right to take it apart, mod it, repair it, tap dance in the code, or hook it up to your personal brand of Arduino kung-fu.

But if you want the right to tinker, you'll have to start fighting for it. Fight for your right to mod and make. Fight for your right to repair. Fight for your right to own your own things.

We live in a brave new digital world, and it's time that we join forces with Cory Doctorow — and other makers leading the movement to free our hardware — when he says, "This has nothing to do with whether information is free or not — it's all about whether people are free." ●

KYLE WIENS is the co-founder of iFixit (ifixit.org), the free repair manual. iFixit's open-source community has taught millions of people how to fix everything from iPhones to Volvos.

7 Cornerstones of Making with Kids

MakerKids shares their recipe for a successful makerspace. By Jennifer Turliuk and Andy Forest

TORONTO-BASED MAKERKIDS IS ONE OF THE WORLD'S ONLY MAKERSPACES SPECIFICALLY DESIGNED FOR KIDS, and many people have asked us to share our recipe. We think of it as a brunch — there are many ways to make it delicious. Take the pieces of our recipe that work for you and make it your own. We're also available to help with this — we envision a future where there are MakerKids chapters all over the world.

MakerKids

The MakerKids Recipe

1. Dedicated Space: Even if just a cart, having a space that's set up to be inspiring and safe allows kids to feel like they have permission to take ownership and be creative beyond what's normally accepted or expected of them.

2. Real Tools: We have the same real tools that any adult makerspace would have. Kids as young as 3 use drills, saws, and soldering irons. To the frequent question "Can you do this for me? You're better at it than me," our answer is "That's why you should do it! Then you'll get as good as me." We'd rather help them learn to do it safely and become more comfortable, or find another way to achieve their goals. This helps them to develop feelings of competence, responsibility, and leadership.

3. Process Over Product: Value experiential learning. We celebrate the fact that they're making, not just what they make. The point is not to take home some shiny object that they've made. We emphasize that it's okay to fail — it's just an opportunity to learn.

A major part of making is researching how to accomplish goals. Instead of telling kids step-by-step instructions, we encourage them to figure out how to do it themselves, ask other kids, or research it online. We frequently answer the question

"How do I do this?" with "Google will tell you!"

4. Interest-Driven: We try to let kids' creative interests define projects as much as possible. If we tell them exactly what to make and how, they quickly lose interest. If they're following their creative interests, they're much more engaged.

Recently, a group of kids were very interested in vehicles, so they designed and built a hovercraft. They learned a lot of skills as they went along: 3D printing (for the lift turbine), motors, Arduino programming, and more. When it failed to get off the ground on the first try, they got right to work reinventing the skirt to reduce weight and optimizing the turbine airflow.

Every activity we do, no matter how short, we incorporate something creative, something open-ended. Let them make it their own!

5. Kids Teaching: We encourage kids to share their knowledge with each other and with their teachers. A low student-to-teacher ratio is valuable in any learning environment, so encourage everyone to be teachers. Kids teaching also gain so much self-confidence. When a new kid asks how to hook up an LED and another kid says, "I can show you that," everyone is growing.

As the kids grow as makers and teachers, we encourage them to volunteer

as helpers in classes. The next step is for them to lead classes themselves.

Sometimes kids know more than we do, especially on topics they're passionate about. In our *Minecraft* classes, the kids are the experts and we learn from them all the time. We make sure to listen and let them teach us, too.

6. Exhibition: Each program has a presentation to the parents, which kids get really excited about. It helps them to organize their thoughts, knowing that at the end of their project, they'll have to explain it to someone else. Having a deadline also helps them focus and move forward.

7. Community: We connect to the Toronto community and the global maker community through events like Maker Faire, local community festivals, school fun fairs, participation in online discussions, and interfacing with folks from other maker companies. We work with many other kids' organizations — for example, we've worked with kids in a music program to build props for their performance. Find out what the makers in your community are passionate about and connect with them.

So that's the summary of our recipe — the mix that makes our youth makerspace work. We want to know how we can help you to do making with kids in your community. We're developing curriculum modules for summer camps, after-school programs, schools, and more. Our board of advisors includes the CEOs of Maker Media and Arduino, and we've developed curriculum modules for clients and sponsors such as Intel and 3D Systems. Email us at info@makerkids.ca. ◑

JENNIFER TURLIUK and **ANDY FOREST** are co-executive directors of MakerKids (makerkids.ca).

MADE ON EARTH

The world of backyard technology

Know a project that would be perfect for Made on Earth?
Email us: *editor@makezine.com*

THE AMAZING, BLAZING EL PULPO MECANICO

ELPULPOMECANICO.COM

A cephalopod like no other, *El Pulpo Mecanico* is a 25-foot-tall mechanical octopus made from found objects and scrap iron that spews fire from its tentacles while eight eyes pop in and out of its head. The brainchild of Eureka, California-based artist **Duane Flatmo**, with electrical panels and flame effects by **Jerry Kunkel**, *El Pulpo* was originally conceived and built for the Burning Man festival of 2011, and it also delighted thousands at Maker Faire Bay Area in May of 2014.

Flatmo's experience as a professional large-scale mural painter and involvement in the annual Kinetic Sculpture Race for the past 32 years gave him a solid foundation to build *El Pulpo*. The scale was derived from the 55-gallon drum tentacles, and the entire piece was made from rusty junk metal with embellishments of silver steel and aluminum. Flatmo notes, "I have a great working relationship with Bonnie at our local scrapyard, Arcata Scrap and Salvage."

El Pulpo is mobile, with the lower chassis built on an extended Ford Econoline van with a 460 V8 engine. As for the flame effects, the sculpture can hold 200 gallons of propane, which "lasts about four hours if we don't hit the fire buttons too much," says Flatmo. "The connection with the sculpture becomes so pronounced when you have all the firepower at your fingertips. It's actually half fire and half percussion. You can play this thing like an instrument."

— *Goli Mohammadi*

+ Read Make:'s interview with Duane Flatmo: makezine.com/elpulpo

Jason Mongue

Duane Flatmo

FULLY MOTORIZED LEGO ASTROMECH DROID

FLICKR.COM/PHOTOS/VMLN8R
Vimal Patel's *Star Wars*-inspired Lego robot rolls around on tank treads, rotates its head, and even breaks out a manipulator that folds back into the body of the robot when not in use.

It uses only parts from Lego's Technic and Power Functions product lines, a detail sure to appeal to Lego fans who insist on solely using official elements in their models. Given these constraints, Patel did a great job of capturing the spirit of the movie robots. Patel, of Lower Hutt, New Zealand, packed the robot full of parts, with more than 630 beams, connectors, and other elements jammed into the robot's small body, including a complicated gearbox that moves all the parts. There are some fun details, including the fold-out third leg that is often overlooked in fan recreations.
— *John Baichtal*

+ Want to build your own? Patel thoughtfully shares the Lego Digital Designer .LXF file (makezine.com/legobot/) so you can see how he built it.

Vimal Patel

JUDGE ME BY MY SIZE, DO YOU?
FLICKR.COM/PHOTOS/PACOALLEN

Paco Allen

San Mateo, California-based intrepid papa **Paco Allen** spent three months crafting this stellar Hoth Luke costume, complete with homemade tauntaun, for his four-year-old daughter. Dismayed at the lack of *Empire Strikes Back* costumes available, Allen combined scratch-built parts with modified off-the-shelf ones to great effect. His daughter had her heart set on a tauntaun, which proved to be the most challenging part. The body, neck, and tail are made from cardboard tubes and the head from newspaper and tape. In a stroke of genius, Allen "cut up a rubber sheep mask and glued it on in pieces to make the snout shorter, the face wider, and the eyelids look more like a tauntaun." He then airbrushed the face, covered the whole thing in fake fur, fashioned the saddle, and made faux legs out of pants stuffed with cotton. To boot, "the legs are jointed at the hip so they swivel when the 'rider' walks."
— *Goli Mohammadi*

LUMBER HACK

MAKEZINE.COM/RAUSCHER

Picture it: A giant supermarket claw machine, but instead of a metal hand with a frustratingly weak grip, it's a real-life chainsaw. In place of stuffed animals, there are stumps of wood on the cutting floor, ready for ripping.

Montreal thinker-maker **Morgan Rauscher** built just such a machine, called Art-Bot. "I made Art-Bot to try to expand the hand with a cybernetic perceptual-prosthetic," Rauscher explains. Suspended inside the polycarbonate acoustic-deflection chamber is an 8-foot-long Arduino-controlled robotic arm built from recycled bicycle components. The user controls the arm with playful arcade game buttons on an external dashboard. A haptic-vibrotactile force feedback system lets the user "feel" the material that the robot touches.

Built in an impressive window of just two months, Rauscher considered many different tools for Art-Bot before settling on a chainsaw. The original plan combined an axe and a chainsaw to form "a kind of hyperactive axe tool thing," but the kickback from the ax's chopping motion forced the arm out of alignment, so that plan was nixed. "Basically, the tool was too badass for the arm," he jokes.

Rauscher's favorite reaction to Art-Bot? "Seeing the anticipation in the eyes of the children as they line up to use it — and then seeing their eyes open wider when they get the chance to control it."

— *Laura Cochrane*

+ Read more about how Rauscher built Art-Bot: makezine.com/artbot

BIGGER WHEEL

CNCKING.COM

Too big for your old Big Wheel? Get back in the race by building an adult-sized trike from plywood.

Jon Cantin, a self-taught designer in Perth, Australia with a passion for CNC fabrication, scaled up the classic kid mobile's design to fit his frame and support his weight. "I want this to be strong, functional, and cool!" The finished project, about 5 feet long by 3 feet wide, uses no hardware — only "a herd of cattle hooves worth of glue" — to assemble its 237 parts cut from 10 sheets of plywood.

Cantin tinkered through design challenges using mental calculations and Autodesk software so he would only have to build the trike once. As his ShopBot Desktop CNC router limited the size of pieces he could cut, the design incorporates overlapping tiles so the front wheel could live up to its big title.

In a series of posts on his website, Cantin talks through the thought processes behind the design, the challenges of building it, and what could be improved next time. The site sells plans for this and other rad projects and freely offers advice and inspiration about CNC skills and entrepreneurship.

— *Gregory Hayes*

Audacious by Design

PROJECT H GIVES
KIDS TOOLS, SKILLS,
AND CONFIDENCE.

Interview by Stett Holbrook
Photographed by Jeffrey Braverman

STETT HOLBROOK
is editor of the
Bohemian, an
alternative weekly in
Santa Rosa, California.
He is a former
senior editor
at Maker Media.

**BERKELEY, CALIFORNIA'S PROJECT H
OFFERS A WINDOW INTO THE FUTURE OF
K-12 EDUCATION.** And if it's not the future, it
should be. Just don't call it a shop class.

Architect Emily Pilloton founded Project H out
of a desire to do something more meaningful
with her skills. That desire grew into a mission
to offer kids the opportunity to explore what they
can do with both their minds and their hands.
Project H aims to use "the power of creativity,
design, and hands-on building to amplify the raw
brilliance of youth, transform communities, and

improve K-12 public education from within."

In a unique partnership with Berkeley's pro-
gressive REALM charter school, Project H offers
a design and build curriculum called Studio H for
middle and high school students. While students
learn to use radial saws, laser cutters, and welding
torches, Pilloton hopes the confidence and self-
knowledge they develop become a transformative force in their lives and communities. She also
spearheaded a build camp for girls called Camp H.

We spoke to Pilloton about Project H ("Humanity,
Happiness, Health, and Habitats,") and her work.

> **" NO GIRL SHOULD HAVE TO FEEL LIKE THEY HAVE TO DUMB THEMSELVES DOWN OR HIDE THEIR BRILLIANCE. "**

What is Project H?

Project H is a nonprofit design organization that I started in 2008. It was founded on the loose idea that design can make people's lives better and, more specifically, it can be audacious. It can be focused on social issues and it can excite young people in a way — inside and outside of school — that is meaningful to them, is meaningful to their communities, and that helps them bring ideas to life in ways that they maybe didn't think were possible.

The documentary *If You Build It* highlights Project H's experience in North Carolina. Can you summarize your experience there?

In 2009 we got cold emailed from a school superintendent in Greenville, N.C.: Dr. Chip Zullinger. He had seen a project we did called the Learning Landscape, which is an educational playground system. There are about 40 of them built around the world. They're made from reclaimed tires, and you can play academic games within this playground, so it's an outdoor playground, a classroom, and a dynamic space for elementary and middle school education.

Dr. Zullinger had seen that project published in a design publication and invited us to come down and basically bring design as a resource to his school district, which was broken. It was one of the poorest performing in the state, and he was on this mission to change it and to use resources that the district hadn't traditionally been looking at, like design, to infuse a new kind of change and excitement for the kids and the teachers.

So we went down there, built four of these playgrounds in four days, and then discovered that Dr. Zullinger was this amazing renegade of an educational leader and had a whole list of other projects for us. To make a long story very short, we discovered a real love for Bertie County and for working with Dr. Zullinger. At a certain point, we just felt like we had to put design in the classroom and that the only real way to influence a school district using design is for it to be part of the academic experience of the students.

How did the partnership with REALM Charter School come about?

As we were realizing our tenure in Bertie County was not going to be as long lasting as we thought it might, for a whole host of

reasons, I had been in conversation with Victor Diaz, founder and executive director of REALM [Revolutionary Education and Learning Movement] charter school. REALM's charter is written around project-based learning and creativity and design, so he had reached out to me, after having heard about Project H through a mutual friend.

We knew that REALM was a place not only where our ideas would be rallied around, but that it would also be a place for us to grow, thrive, and try new things and experiment and push the boundaries of what Project H could be.

We're in our second year at REALM, and we have 216 students in 8th, 9th, 10th, and 11th grade. We're building the school library. We built a classroom out of shipping containers last year. We're deploying geodesic domes around the city — just all kinds of crazy stuff. And I also started an after-school and over-the-summer girl's camp called Camp H for 4th, 5th, 6th, and 7th graders.

It's just an amazing school community to be a part of, where we can really push on our own practice, and see how much of this really works in the tight constraints of an urban public charter school with a very unique school population.

We're in Berkeley, but most of our kids come from Richmond and Oakland, and a lot of them are English language learners. There's a high percentage of special education students, so we really see it as an amazing opportunity to offer something different to kids looking for or needing something different from their school.

What personal experiences helped shape the creation of Project H?

Project H grew out of my own dissatisfaction with the status quo and just being really sick of doing work that wasn't meaningful to me and that didn't seem to be meaningful to anyone else. In the greater sense, the usual client-designer relationship is often based on luxury, money, privilege, and not that that's a bad thing necessarily, but for me the thing that got me excited about design as a kid — and more specifically about architecture — was the problem-solving, the kind of MacGyver-style eagerness of solving a problem in the moment under tight constraints. I love being constrained — having $10, one hand tied behind my back, and being blindfolded, having nothing and making something beautiful out of that.

I grew up in an extremely affluent, mostly white neigh-

borhood, and as a woman of color, I experienced my childhood with the lens of not belonging and having to really forge my own way to make meaning. The way I did that was often through very physical and tactile means, through building, exploring in the forest, and competitive sports.

Project H was kind of just an extension of feeling dissatisfied in my own career, knowing there was a different way to do it, not knowing how to do it, but thinking that if I set up a nonprofit and have to answer to the IRS and the Secretary of the State in California, then I'm going to figure it out and I have to.

How is it funded?

Project H is funded through a revolving and always evolving jigsaw puzzle of private foundation grants, the National Endowment for the Arts, and some public funding, as well as corporate sponsorships, in-kind donations of tools, materials, and equipment, and a broad base of either crowdfunded or small-scale donations that are more project-based.

How is Project H different from a traditional shop class?

Vocational education was born out of the trades, out of needing to train the next generation of workers for specific skill sets — masons, welders, etc. — and unfortunately in a lot of communities (we saw this in Bertie County), vocational education was a track intended mostly for kids who were not college-bound. And in a place like Bertie County, that often meant the black kids, so vocational ed became this weird fulcrum that really divided a lot of kids into the high-performing kids (often the white kids), the affluent kids that were going on to college, and then the rest of them. And as a class, vocational education has been based mostly on skills rather than critical thinking about why we're using those skills in the first place.

The tag line for Studio H is "design, build, transform." So while vocational education has traditionally only been focused on the build

> **VOCATIONAL EDUCATION HAS BEEN BASED MOSTLY ON SKILLS RATHER THAN CRITICAL THINKING ABOUT WHY WE'RE USING THOSE SKILLS IN THE FIRST PLACE.**

portion — like how we train the next generation of brick masons — we really believe that no kid should build anything that they have not designed themselves, and no kid should build anything that doesn't have some kind of meaning for a community beyond themselves.

In other words, I'm never going to hand a kid a set of drawings and say go build this birdhouse. I say birdhouse because we have built birdhouses in my girl's camp, but every girl designs their own birdhouse with a very specific bird in mind, and it's intended to be placed in a specific ecosystem for the benefit of a local community garden.

There's a way to still teach those skills, but to infuse meaning for the person building it, and then also for the community in which it exists. I think that shop classes in the future, Studio H included, are going to be less about trades and less about skill building and more about meaning, personal voice, and the community — what we're building, why, for whom, and why it's an extension of our own ideas. That's the difference.

The other thing I would say is that most people think of shop classes as really low-tech, like here's a chisel and a saw. We have all those things, and our students know how to use the most basic old school hand planes, but we also have a laser cutter. We use CNC technology, and there's really no difference. I don't think one is more important than the other.

We did these laser-etched skateboards that had to be pressed in a 20,000-pound bottle jack press that we welded out of steel. And we had to use a band saw and a table saw and a router to cut them, and then we laser-etched them, and every single step of that, the low tech and the high tech were just as important.

What do you say to parents who wonder why their kids are learning "blue collar" skills?

I ask them, "Well, are they really?" Because they just went to Carl Bass' shop, the CEO of Autodesk, and saw a crazy CNC router that

THERE'S A WAY TO STILL TEACH THOSE SKILLS, BUT TO INFUSE MEANING FOR THE PERSON BUILDING IT.

exists nowhere else in the country. I don't see them as blue-collar skills necessarily. I think what we are teaching kids is the broadest array of skills they could possibly imagine, so that when they wake up one morning and they say "I want to build a skyscraper that goes from here to the moon," they feel like, "OK, I've got 50 tools that I know how to use to at least see if that's possible." I don't think they are blue-collar skills so much as the agency to pull from a wide variety of tools to make anything possible.

How does Project H engage girls in traditional male-oriented activities?

Camp H, which is the after-school and summer girls' program, is really my baby. It's the thing for me that feels really personal, really special, and really intimate because I remember being a 10-year-old misfit girl and being really good at math and being really good at a lot of things and still feeling like I didn't belong and that it wasn't cool to know how to do stuff. No girl should have to feel like they have to dumb themselves down or hide their brilliance, and nothing against boys, but it's kind of ballsy for a 10-year-old girl to leave our camp saying, "I just learned how to weld" and there are boys around going "What? How come we didn't get to do that?" I love that.

I think pulling girls out of the coed class into a girl's-only space, they just have a totally different way that they approach making when there's no social tension around it, there's no "oh it looks like the boys go first" — they all pick up a welder and weld you under a table. They become much more confident and then they carry that confidence back into everything else.

So I have also been really intentional about doing things that are not in any way girlie. We will not be making jewelry boxes. I am not going to paint a drill pink. I am not going to give them the girl version of the toolbox. They weld with the same Lincoln Electric welder that our high school students use. I want them to feel like they are equals.

What do you hope kids get out of Project H?

I really want every kid to leave Project H thinking "I can't believe that was even possible and I really can't believe that we pulled it off" because that sense of agency and that sense of power, and the sense of confidence that going through your life anything is not only possible but totally achievable, that's what these kids need at this age.

I see it in my camp girls after they weld. These are 9-year-old girls who weld and fuse metal and they leave feeling like "I just fused metal — don't you dare tell me there's something I can't do." I love that. I love giving kids a little bit of a chip on their shoulder, but in a positive way. ◐

+ Check out Project H at projecthdesign.org.

PROJECT H SHARES LESSON PLANS AND ACTIVITIES ON THEIR SITE

They write, "By open-sourcing our own learning, our failures, our adaptations, and our content, we hope to create a more transparent and boundary-pushing community of educators and creatives."Here are a few examples. See them all at *PROJECTHDESIGN.ORG/TOOLBOX*.

ROCK CLIMBING HAND HOLDS

Use the architecture of the human hand to make wall-mountable hand holds using a traditional sculpting, molding, and casting process.

RIGHT ANGLE BIRDHOUSES
Learn all the basic woodshop tools by building a unique, 90°-based wooden birdhouse.

CONSTRUCTED SIGNAGE

Develop the capacity for seeing potential, develop and practice collaboration, and foster ownership through action.

DUG NORTH creates kinetic sculptures made primarily of wood that employ a hand-cranked mechanism to animate a scene. Dug is also the voice behind The Automata Blog (AutomataBlog.com). He writes a quarterly column about automaton-making and is sought out as a subject-matter expert on the topic.

FROM CUBICLE TO CLOCK REPAIR

Written by Dug North • Photography by Shannon Murphy

HOW I TOOK THE LEAP TO FOLLOWING MY PASSIONS.

BEING A DEDICATED AUTOMATON MAKER, I started to learn how to repair antique clocks because it seemed like a good way to commune with the master automaton-makers of old. I didn't expect that it would turn into an occupation that would allow me to leave my cubicle-based job for good, but a few factors made it possible.

PREPARING FOR THE LEAP

In some respects, I've been preparing for this change in jobs for a long time. I've saved some money. I've amassed a huge collection of tools. I've taken courses on small business, jewelry making, machine tools, and wood finish repair. Over the last couple of years, I've also taken a bunch of clock repair courses with the National Association of Watch and Clock Collectors (NAWCC).

JUST PLAIN LUCKY

In one important respect, I just got lucky. By chance, I met Bob Frishman, owner of Andover, Massachusetts-based Bell-Time Clocks, at an antique show. Bob has been collecting, fixing, and selling clocks for 33 years and is active in the horological world. I got to know Bob, and he eventually asked me if I'd ever considered doing clock repair for a living. With Bob's invaluable guidance, I took the leap in July of 2013, and I love my new job.

MAKING THINGS

I don't feel like I've accomplished anything if I can't point to something tangible at the end of the day that I either made or fixed. Clock repair requires both fixing and making — mostly with wood and brass, my two favorite materials.

LEARNING EVERY SINGLE DAY

There are so many different types of clocks, with so many different possible problems, that I'll never know all there is to know. I like that. Every day I gain new knowledge — some of it handed to me, some hard-won.

KEEPING A VENERABLE TRADE ALIVE

There aren't enough qualified clock repairers these days, and few schools teach the trade. However, the clocks are still around. If they aren't cared for, I fear they'll be scrapped. I can't claim to possess exceptional expertise or a long, illustrious career, but I'm proud to be next in a long line of clock repairers.

THE TOOLS

The tools of the trade are so diverse, so specific, so traditional, and so arcane. I love them all. My favorite is my watchmaker's lathe, also an antique, made in nearby Waltham, Massachusetts.

IT FITS WITH WHERE I LIVE

On the two-block walk from my home to my repair shop, I walk on cobblestone streets, past old brick buildings and an old steam locomotive, within sight of a large tower clock, and over a canal that once powered the textile mills of Lowell, Massachusetts. Many consider the city to be the cradle of the Industrial Revolution in the United States, and the entire downtown is a National Historical Park. Working on old machines in this setting, I feel connected to the history that surrounds me.

NEW UNDERSTANDING OF AUTOMATA

My original motivation holds true. I've seen some antique clockwork automata for a second time recently and realized that I understood what I was seeing in a new way. I now know the names of those funny little parts, what they do, and how they were fabricated. More importantly, I know why a clockmaker would be uniquely qualified to make a lifelike machine. Eventually, I'll incorporate what I've learned into my own automata.

CUSTOMERS ACTUALLY WANT TO SEE ME

When you visit your car mechanic, you may or may not be there by choice. Sometimes you simply must get your car running again. It's not the same with clock repair. Customers have definitely made a choice to have their clock fixed. They have a complicated, delicate machine that they treasure for whatever reason. Perhaps it's clever, perhaps it's beautiful, or perhaps it belonged to a grandmother. Perhaps all three things are true. It's an honor to be entrusted with these heirlooms and gratifying to see a customer's face when they hear their clock chime for the first time in years. ◉

+ See more of Dug's work at AutomataBlog.com and at ClockFix.com.

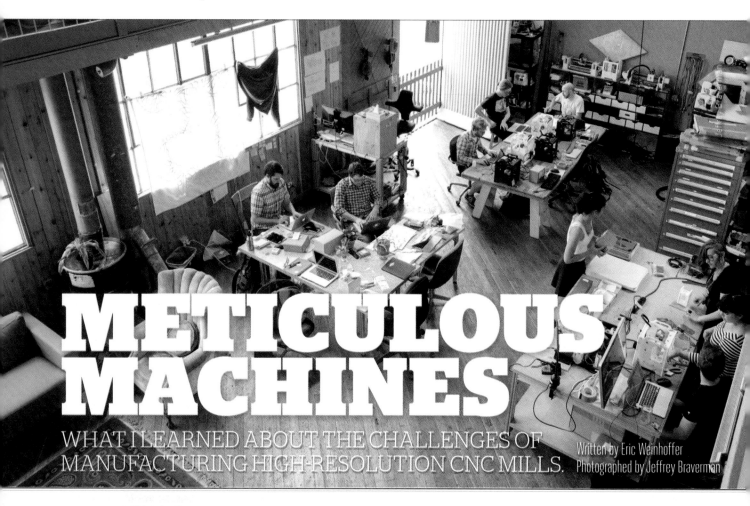

METICULOUS MACHINES

WHAT I LEARNED ABOUT THE CHALLENGES OF MANUFACTURING HIGH-RESOLUTION CNC MILLS.

Written by Eric Weinhoffer
Photographed by Jeffrey Braverman

ERIC WEINHOFFER
is a manufacturing engineer at Other Machine Co., where he uses big machines to make tiny machines. When not building things, Eric enjoys skiing, cycling, and climbing.

IN MID-MARCH, I STARTED WORKING AT SAN FRANCISCO STARTUP OTHER MACHINE CO., after more than a year and a half working as a product development engineer for the Maker Shed. During that period, I learned a lot about e-commerce, how to bring a variety of products to life through efficient part sourcing, and how to market them effectively once they'd launched. But as my knowledge of product development and management grew, I strove to learn more about the manufacturing processes and engineering required to bring kit components to life.

I knew that working for a startup like OMC would help me get the knowledge I sought, and I was excited to work in a space that reminded me of the machine shop I frequented in college — full of people who are smarter than me, making things that inspire me. So I moved to the Bay and began work in a field I was eager to learn more about: manufacturing desktop computer numerically controlled (CNC) machines.

Our main product, the Othermill, is a desktop-friendly, 16-pound CNC mill designed for precision work. Unlike 3D printers, which deposit plastic material from a nozzle in an additive process, mills do the opposite, removing material using a high-speed cutting tool. This subtractive process allows the mill to build parts from a much wider range of materials. It can cut anything softer than the cutting tool itself, and often in much less time than a 3D printer could print the object.

When I started, I figured I had a passable grasp on what it meant to bring a great product to life, but I was wrong. In the past, I'd often look at technical specifications on product pages without thinking about the challenges of actually achieving them on a repeatable basis. I typically thought, "Oh, resolution down to 1/1000 of an inch. I could make some really dimensionally accurate parts with that thing." Have you ever thought about what it takes to get there, every single time? Neither had I.

LEAVE NOTHING TO CHANCE

The frame of the Othermill is the most critical component, and we produce each one in-house on a Haas CNC router. Since the overall look, feel, and ease of assembly of the machine is dependent on the HDPE frame, we handle the stock HDPE sheets with the utmost care. Ideally, each frame ends up exactly the same post-machining. Unfortunately, some things are out of our control. I learned early on to not trust the thickness tolerances provided by plastic suppliers — we've seen sheets vary by up to $\frac{1}{32}$ of an inch, which is huge when many of our features are depth-dependent. Nevertheless, we protect the stack of sheets from dust and other airborne particles in the shop with a plastic cover, and each sheet is wiped down before mounting on the router bed.

We even installed antiglare covers on the windows of the shop, in case the temperature change between their cool storage spot and the heat of the morning sun on the router bed might cause thermal deformation. No specific occurrences point to the sun as a possible culprit of strange dimensional changes, but you can't leave anything to chance.

CONTROL YOUR QUALITY VIGOROUSLY

I quickly learned that serious attention to detail is required to repeatedly and reliably hit the resolutions we're after. I was immediately thrown into the world of quality control (QC) and the tools used to complete it effectively. We use pin gauges — cylinders of steel ground down to extremely precise diameters — to check the size of the critical features in each frame as it comes off the router bed, and we use digital micrometers to check the thickness of the features that hold the machine together. Deviations of 1/1000 of an inch in diameter, differences you'd never notice without QC tools like the gauges, can lead us to scrapping the part, which is a serious cost and time drain, especially for a startup like us.

The second most critical component of the mill is the spindle assembly, which contains the precision bearings, shaft, and the motor that rapidly rotates the cutting tool. The bearings inside the spindle assembly allow the shaft to spin freely and, hopefully, perfectly perpendicular to the bed. Any play in the assembly causes spindle "runout" (a slight wiggle), leading to less accurate cuts. We work to avoid this in every spindle assembly we produce by not only constantly refining the manufacturing process, but also by testing different ways to put them together.

Since any play in the assembly isn't warranted, we've tested various adhesives, set times, and loads for pressing everything together. Once we're confident that the spindle is in tip-top shape, we have each machine "face," or cut a small layer of material off its own aluminum bed, to ensure that the bed and the spindle are perfectly perpendicular to each other. The most painful part of my job is seeing an assembled mill, which we put so much time and effort into producing, fail the QC process due to a bad part. And thus, controlling the quality of the components is absolutely key.

PLAN AHEAD AND AUTOMATE

Once I was able to get in the shop and help out with production, the significance of designing with manufacturing in mind became clear, especially when dealing with large quantities. Relocating the posi-

tion of certain components on the router bed during machining or changing the design of a part in CAD can shave precious seconds off production time. And when shipping machines is a priority, every second counts.

Beginning with the right components saves tons of time as well. Finding parts that are easy to install during assembly and work properly over a long period is critical to preventing customer service issues down the line. One of my early tasks was to complete HALT, or "highly accelerated life testing," on a potential limit switch for the next version of the machine. The limit switch is what notifies the software when each axis has reached its limit. To do so, I modified a current motor assembly to accept the new limit switch and wrote a few simple lines of code to continuously and repeatedly ram the spindle assembly into the switch, for hundreds of cycles, to ensure it would still operate after being put through harsh circumstances. We'd eventually like to run an Othermill continuously until it stops working, hopefully after days, while keeping an eye on it with a Raspberry Pi, sensors, and a webcam.

It became clear that creating jigs and adding automation wherever possible is an incredible way to save time as well. Instead of fastening certain components down with bolts during machining, for example, we're working towards a future of press-fit pins, so the pieces can just be popped into place in seconds.

BE PREPARED FOR PROBLEMS

No matter how much you plan ahead, things are going to go wrong. We recently experienced a rare lightning storm in San Francisco, which sent a power surge through the building and knocked the life out of our most valuable tool: the frame-producing Haas CNC router. It was down for a gut-wrenching week and a half, during which we had to do whatever it took to continue prototyping parts for the next version of the Othermill. So, I cut a test part for the Othermill on the Othermill itself. Finding creative solutions to inevitable problems like this is imperative if you want to keep pushing forward.

After only a short time, I've learned more about the production and design of a high-quality product than I thought I would in a whole year. Working with a small team in a fast-paced environment like this is extremely exciting, challenging, and a ton of fun. Also, learning how to use the tools in the shop from two female engineers, the colleagues with whom I work most closely, is a refreshing change of pace from the engineering "norm."

Our team encounters problems every day that we solve by building or modifying something to fix it, and that sort of spontaneous making out of necessity is what I've enjoyed most so far. My preconceptions about manufacturing a high-resolution product have shifted as I've been exposed to the challenges of getting it done, and my appreciation for the quality of the mass-produced hardware around me has skyrocketed as a result. ◗

GEEK CLUB

Illustrated by Jing Zhang

BIG TOOLS, HUGE BUILDS, SAVVY SUPPORT — MAKERSPACES HELP YOU LEVEL UP.

FROM TECHSHOPS TO FAB LABS, MAKERSPACES ARE POPPING UP AROUND THE COUNTRY AND THE WORLD, helping makers gain experience, develop support networks, and build bigger and better than ever before. Volunteer-run or professional, membership- or employee-based, non- or for-profit, they're offering tools, education, and space to makers who don't have a home shop or who want to go beyond it.

Part recreational shop, part product incubator, part R&D lab, part community center, they cater to — and help define — a growing, decentralized hub of the maker world. These are places where makers are safe, welcome, comfortable, and free to pursue their goals, where innovation and creativity is fostered, learning is encouraged, and community trumps just about everything.

In these pages you'll see some makerspaces up close, as well as look at what they can do and how they're growing. You'll see some of their tools and their builds, and maybe you'll be inspired to check one out in your area. Welcome to the Geek Club.

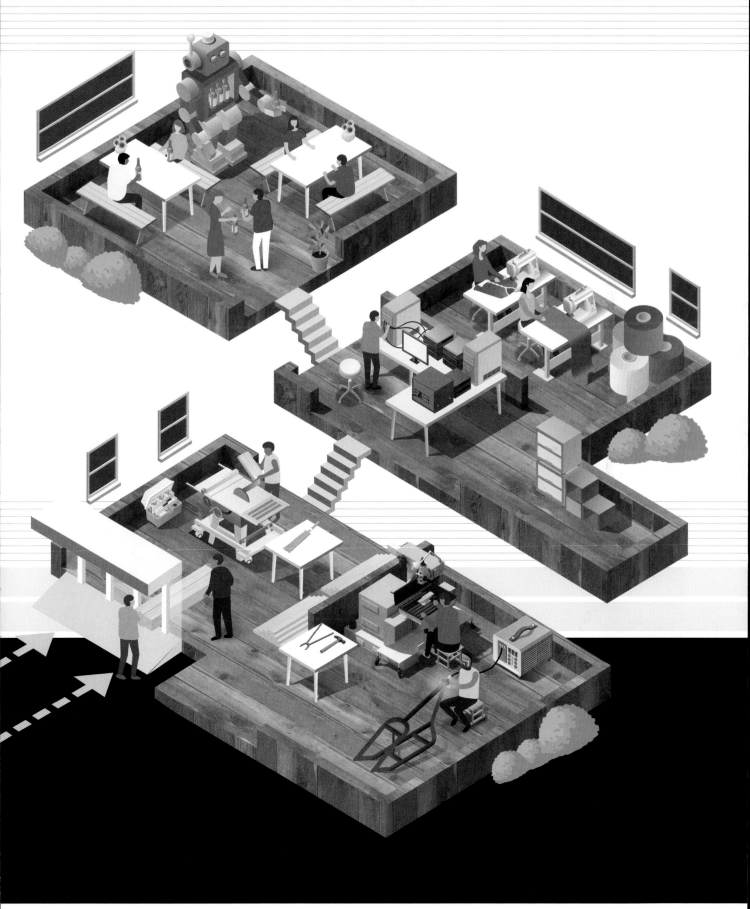

RICK SCHERTLE
schertle@yahoo.com
teaches middle school
in San Jose, California,
and is a regular
Make: contributor.
He is founder of
the Washington
Maker Workshop,
and co-founder of
AirRocketWorks.com.
Along with his wife
and kids, he loves all
things that fly.

LENDY DUNAWAY
is a lifelong lover of
designing and building
things, and a collector
of the tools, hardware,
and machines to do
it with. After writing
software for 20 years,
he now runs a small
industrial design and
fabrication company
in San Jose, California,
where he hosts a
Young Makers club.

RAISE A CNC'ED MAKERSPACE SHED

Written by Rick Schertle and Lendy Dunaway

BUILD A BIG, CUSTOMIZABLE, STAND-ALONE WORKSHOP WITH CNC-CUT TRUSSES FOR ABOUT $1,000.

ONE OF MY BIG PROJECTS THIS YEAR WAS TO OPEN A MAKERSPACE FOR KIDS IN A LOW-INCOME AREA OF SAN JOSE, CALIFORNIA (washingtonmakerworkshop.org). There was a small garage on the property, but we needed a larger structure where the classes could meet.

We figured a 14-by-16-foot space (224 square feet) would be about ideal.

I researched a number of quick-build designs but didn't really find one to meet my needs, so I ran the idea by my friend Lendy Dunaway, who's involved in the Young Makers program (youngmakers.org) and is an expert fabricator. In Lendy's shop, his signature piece of equipment is an industrial-size CNC router with a 5-by-10-foot cutting bed. He offered to design an inexpensive structure using custom-made trusses with very little scrap wood left over.

Here the results of our design and building process: the CNC Makerspace Shed. The shed is big enough to seat 16 people comfortably at worktables, and it can accommodate a huge 8-foot-high roll-up door. While we use it for a makerspace, with a transparent roof to admit natural light, it can easily be customized into something that works for you — and whatever your needs or weather conditions may require.

1. BUILD THE TRUSSES AND BRACKETS

1A. Download the DXF drawing from the project page at makezine.com/cnc-makerspace-shed and transform it to toolpaths using your favorite CAM software. Then cut the truss parts out of 10 sheets of ⁷/₁₆" OSB using a CNC router. Each sheet, along with four 2×4s, makes one truss.

NOTE: IF YOU DON'T HAVE A CNC ROUTER, YOU CAN CUT THESE PARTS WITH A CIRCULAR SAW OR EVEN A HANDSAW.

1B. Cut the 2×4s according to the cut diagram pictured here.

1C. Glue and screw the trusses together with the 2×4s sandwiched in between as shown here, using 1⁵/₈" screws and following the screw pattern in the DXF drawing.

1D. Rout the edges of the trusses for a neat finished look.

1E. Find some large scrap "angle iron" at a metal yard and cut it into 40 pieces 6" long. Anything bigger than 2½" on each side will work. We found some nice aluminum angles that were 2½"×3". Cutting your own should save a good deal of money.

1F. Measure, mark, and drill a pair of ¹¹/₃₂" or ³/₈" holes through each side of each bracket as shown, centered to (roughly) match the spacing shown on the DXF drawing. (Your angle iron may vary.) All holes should be "mirror-images" so that the brackets will line up with one another, no matter which way you install them.

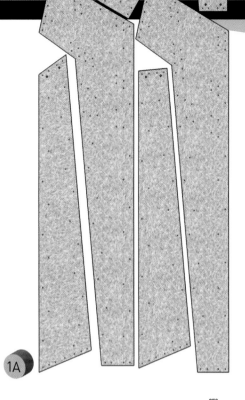

1A

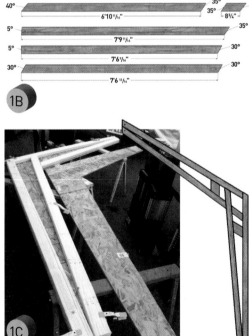

1C

1E

Time Required:
A Few Weekends
Cost:
$850–$1,500

Materials
This list of materials cost us $849 excluding doors, roof, and walls.
» Lumber, 2×4 (nominal), 8' lengths (40)
» Lumber, 2×6 (nominal): 8' lengths (30); 14' lengths (3), 16' lengths (4)
» Lumber, 2×10 (nominal), 16' length
» OSB (oriented strand board), ²³/₃₂", 4'×8' sheets (8)
» OSB, ⁷/₁₆", 4'×8' sheets (14)
» Piers, concrete, 8"×8"×8" (12) with wood block top
» Joist hanger brackets, 2×6 (48)
» Wood glue, 1gal
» Wood screws or deck screws, 1⁵/₈", 25lbs
» Lag screws, ³/₈"×3" (32)
» Bolts, coarse, ⁵/₁₆"×3½" (40)
» Bolts, coarse, ⁵/₁₆"×2½" (16)
» Nuts, coarse, ⁵/₁₆" (56)
» Washers, ³/₈" (144)
» Angle stock, steel or aluminum, 2½"×2½" or bigger, 20' total length aka angle iron
» Roofing materials, wall coverings, and doors of your choice

Tools
» CNC router with 4'×8' bed (optional) You can also cut the trusses with hand or power saws.
» Hacksaw, reciprocating saw, or cutoff saw
» Drill and drill bits for wood and metal
» Socket set
» Handheld circular saw aka Skilsaw
» Leveling tools
» Positive placement nail gun (optional)
» Hammer
» Clamps
» Ladder

Jeffrey Braverman

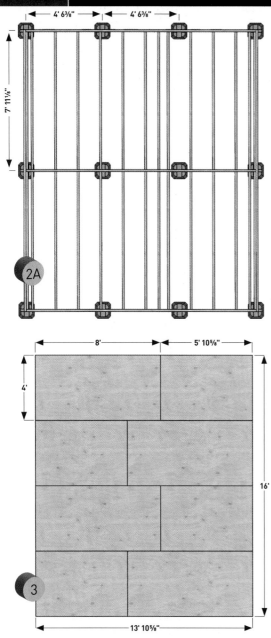

2A

8'   5' 10⅝"

4'

16'

3

13' 10⅝"

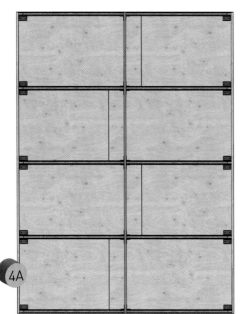

4A

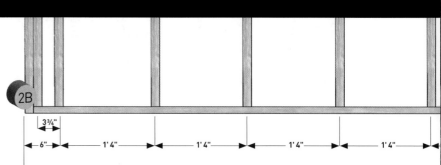

2B

3¾"

6"   1' 4"   1' 4"   1' 4"   1' 4"

4A

4B

2. BUILD THE FLOOR STRUCTURE

2A. Place 12 piers on the ground in the locations designated on the plans and level them. A laser level can be really handy. Dig out or add shims where needed to get them all nice and level.
2B. Frame your floor structure on top of the piers using 2×6s and joist hangers. A "positive placement" nail gun is helpful for installing the joist hangers (the nail tip protrudes so you can see exactly where you're driving it), but it's not required.

3. LAY THE FLOORING

3A. Cut 4 of the ²³/₃₂" OSB panels down to 5' 10-⅝" long.
3B. Then screw down all the ²³/₃₂" panels to the floor joists in the pattern shown here, using 1⅝" screws.

4. RAISE THE TRUSSES

4A. Screw the angle brackets into the floor joists in the locations shown, using 3" lag screws with washers. I built a little jig the width of the trusses to make sure the brackets were the right distance apart.
4B. Mark the 16' ridge beam to match the spacing of the angle brackets on the floor, so that the trusses will line up correctly from the beam to the floor. Then bolt the remaining angle brackets to the beam using 3½" bolts, nuts, and a washer on each side (2 washers per bolt).
4C. Mark and drill all trusses with slightly oversize holes to line up with your bracket holes, Now raise, hold, and bolt the trusses into place through the top brackets and bottom brackets, using 3½" bolts (or 2½" bolts for the trusses at the ends of the building). Raising the trusses requires the help of friends. You need someone in the middle holding up the ridge beam. We clamped the trusses together temporarily to hold them while we got things lined up. This gets a little tricky, especially 12' up on a ladder.
  Install the 2 end trusses first, then the middle truss, and then the final 2.

NOTE: HAVING A RIDGE BEAM THAT IS NOT WARPED HELPS A LOT IN GETTING THINGS LINED UP!

4C

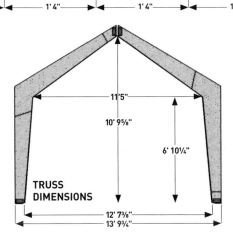

TRUSS DIMENSIONS

11'5"
10' 9⅝"
6' 10¼"
12' 7⅞"
13' 9¾"

9⅜" 6⅝" 10" 3¾"
1' 4" 1' 4" 1' 4" 1' 4" 1' 4"

5. FINISH THE STRUCTURE

Once all the trusses are bolted in place, install 2 sheets of OSB horizontally on the bottom of each side. Before screwing them in, use a level to make sure the trusses are vertical. The plywood should fit perfectly on the 16' length of the workshop.

Two additional sheets of OSB or plywood can be added to each side to fully enclose the sides of the structure.

6. ROOF, DOORS, AND WINDOWS

The shed is structurally complete, but it won't keep the weather out yet.

For natural light, we put clear plastic panels on the roof. Inadvertently, though, we created a greenhouse that was so warm it was virtually unusable. I ended up putting in rigid foam insulation on the sunny side. That did the trick!

The ends can be framed and finished however you wish. We put in an 8'-wide, 7½'-tall roll-up door on one side (about $500 online), and on the other side, two huge 4'-wide by 5'-high "barn door" windows that swing open for ventilation during warm days.

7. FINISHING TOUCHES

The trusses provide a perfect setup for lots of built-in custom shelving. We're also planning on installing a storage loft on the end opposite the roll-up door. The inside is light, airy, and a very pleasant workspace.

We added pull-down power cords and hanging work lights in the middle of the workshop. Right now we're using folding tables and stools but eventually we'd like to add flexible custom worktables. Also in the works are a giant whiteboard and a large LCD monitor for presentations.

The opportunities to customize the space are limitless. We'd love to see what you do with your custom-built CNC workshop. ◉

Get the plans and CNC drawings, and share your shed at makezine. com/cnc-makerspace-shed
Share it: *#makeprojects*

The Fab Lab House, built at Fab Lab Barcelona

FAB LABS @ 10

Written by Members of The Fab Lab Global Network

TEN YEARS OF MAKING (ALMOST) ANYTHING.

FAB LABS ARE A GLOBAL COMMUNITY OF LOCAL WORKSHOPS that enable invention by providing access to tools and guidance for digital fabrication. The fab lab concept sprang from an overwhelming student response to hands-on making enabled by the digital fabrication tools used in the MIT rapid prototyping class MAS: 863, How to Make (Almost) Anything. A 2001 National Science Foundation grant seeded the first fab labs as an educational outreach program.

Revisiting our story in the premiere issue of Make: magazine, we check back in with the Fab Lab Network team, which has grown to over 250 labs worldwide, about what they've been up to and where the community is headed.

OPEN AND COLLABORATIVE

Fab labs empower individuals with tools, skills, and a knowledgeable community of experts once available only to specialized professions. A single maker can engage in all aspects of digitally fabricating things, from computer-aided design to electronics design, production, and programming, to machining, mold-making, and more. Fab labs share an open and collaborative philosophy and an evolving inventory of core capabilities that allow people and projects to be shared across globally networked local labs.

In early 2005, I read an article about fab labs in the first issue of *Make:* magazine. My reaction at the time was, "Wow, I didn't realize a vinyl cutter

The Fluxamaphonic,
a physical interface to Elliot
Clapp's computer-based FM synthesizer.

Elliot Clapp

is less than $2,000!" We immediately ordered one and started doing our own in-house signage for gallery shows at AS220, a community arts center in Providence, Rhode Island. Ten years later, AS220 Labs is a full digital fabrication lab and a Fab Academy instruction site (see *page 37*) for five years. The Fab Lab Network has achieved a great deal with a consistent vision, conscientious follow-through, and a methodology of embracing chaos.

—**SHAWN WALLACE**, AS220 Labs Director, *Getting Started with Raspberry Pi* co-author, artist, and programmer.

FAB FUTURE

When I did the inaugural interview in *Make:* about fab labs, I had no expectation for the explosive growth that was in store for both. "Making" has grown from a verb to a noun to a movement. And fab labs have been rapidly multiplying ever since, up to a network of hundreds of sites.

In retrospect, there was an inverse relationship between what I thought was easy and hard. The research roadmap to the *Star Trek* replicator is progressing nicely, from computers controlling machines to machines making machines to coding the construction of programmable materials. What was much more difficult was building the organizational capacity to match.

The technological goal of fab labs is to make themselves obsolete, by being able to make fab labs (see Fab 2.0, next page). Their real legacy is likely to be the .org/.com/.edu ecosystem that's emerging to support them. The personalization of fabrication challenges the historical separation of education, industry, infrastructure, aid, and art. This is a historical moment analogous to the appearance of the Internet that required the invention of new organizations to create and connect it. As important as that was, the ability to turn data into things and things into data poses an even larger question that fab labs are helping answer: How will we live, work, and play in a world where anyone can make (almost) anything?

—**NEIL GERSHENFELD**, Originator of the fab labs, Director of MIT's Center for Bits and Atoms and the Fab Academy. Author of *Fab, When Things Start To Think, The Nature of Mathematical Modeling,* and *The Physics of Information Technology.*

FAB CITY

In 2001, the Institute for Advanced Architecture of Catalonia (IAAC) and MIT began to collaboratively explore the impact of information technologies on the homes and cities of the future. We wanted to make Barcelona the first self-sufficient city in the world, using recycled materials to produce all the resources (things, energy, and food) we needed.

Laser-cut woodblock prints produced during a AS220 Labs/Printshop class.

Fab Lab Kamakura, a former sake warehouse repurposed for a new age.

The Fab House produced at Fab Lab Barcelona for the Solar Decathlon Europe uses an intentionally anthropomorphic, climate-passive parametric design.

The implementation of Fab Lab Barcelona was our first step toward empowering a new entrepreneurial middle class. We envisioned a metropolis where our citizens could translate their knowledge directly into production through digital fabrication.

I now work for the Barcelona City Council, where a new class of politicians are reinventing the urban landscape as we scale our fab labs to self-sustaining fab cities.

—**VICENTE GUALLART**, Chief Architect, Barcelona City Council. Founder of the Institute for Advanced Architecture of Catalonia and Fab Lab Barcelona. Author of *The Self-Sufficient City* and *Geologics.*

BEING FAB-ULOUS

Setting up a fab lab involves accessing the right tools for the curriculum. The current recommended inventory costs ~$50,000 in equipment and ~$10,000 in materials and includes:

» A laser cutter for press-fit assembly

» A 4' x 8' CNC router for making large, structural objects like furniture and molds for composites

» A sign cutter, to produce flexible copper circuits, antennas and printing masks

» A precision (micron resolution) milling machine to make 3D molds and surface-mount circuit boards

» Programming tools for low-cost, high-speed embedded processors

» A 3D scanner and printer

» Custom software to run any fab lab machine ("Turn Code Into Things," page 38)

Details at: makezine.com/go/about-fablab

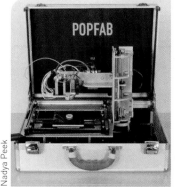

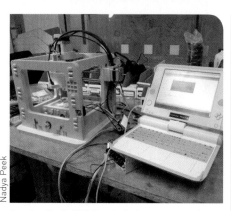

Nadya Peek

The PopFab mill/printer/vinyl cutter in a suitcase by Nadya Peek and Ilan Moyer.

Jonathan Ward's MTM Snap-Lock, the precursor to the Othermill: http://mtm.cba.mit.edu

Anna Kaziunas France

"My Lungs Your Heart", by Lu Heintz. A hand-drawn sketch was scanned, etched into copper plate using Haystacks CNC router, then formed, patined and assembled using traditional metal working techniques.

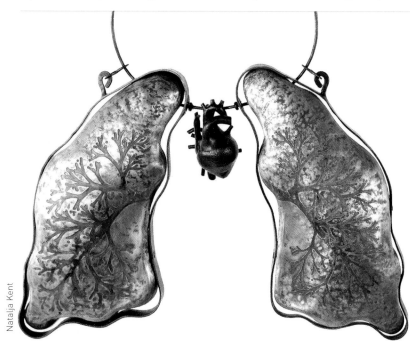

Natalja Kent

FAB 2.0: MACHINES THAT MAKE

Going to a fab lab to use digital fabrication tools is great, but what if you want to use a particular machine all the time or add specific functionality that doesn't exist yet?

It turns out, the accuracy and precision of fab lab equipment is well suited to producing *more* digital fabrication tools. In fact, several companies have fab lab roots, including Ultimaker, Other Machine Co., Formlabs, and Taktia.

To make it easier to create homegrown "Machines That Make" we are developing modular hardware, software (*"Turn Code Into Things,"* page 38) and machine control platforms. In the near future, prototyping a new fabrication machine could be as simple as bolting together standard motion components, networking them in a fab-bus control system, and adapting an in-browser interface.

—**NADYA PEEK**, PhD student at MIT's Center for Bits and Atoms, Machines That Make developer (PopFab, MTM Snap)

FAB ART

Haystack Mountain School of Crafts became involved with the Fab Lab Network in 2009 when I invited Neil Gershenfeld to speak at our conference, Making: Past, Present, and Future. We wanted to examine ways that humans have used technology to create, from the simplest hand tools to digital manufacturing. Gershenfeld brought along a smaller version of a fab lab so conference participants could experience working with computers to make things. While we don't teach traditional crafts, our program is grounded in the traditions of craft — working with our hands to manipulate materials and having a deep understanding of the capabilities of those materials, including clay, metal, fiber, wood, and glass.

Gershenfeld compares bringing digital equipment to Haystack to Bob Dylan going electric at Newport. Many of those in attendance couldn't see the connection between our craft/material world and the digital world. To some of us, though, it seemed an important and vital one to make. The connection is this: Humans are toolmakers and these are new tools. The wisdom in working comes with knowing which tool to use when and what material to use in making work. Our lab has extended ways that we can work and reminds us of our legacy and our future as makers.

—**STUART KESTENBAUM**, Poet and director of the Haystack Mountain School of Crafts in Deer Isle, Maine

FAB10BARCELONA

FAB10 is the 10th international conference, symposium and annual meeting of the Fab Lab Network, an open, creative community of fabricators, artists, scientists, engineers, educators, students, amateurs, and professionals of all ages.

This year's gathering will assemble fabricators from over 250 labs from more than 40 countries. Featured events include live onsite collaborative prototyping of a pavilion, an exhibition of 100 Barcelona-based makers, a Fab Kids program, and a 1,000 square meter "pop up" fabrication facility.

The overarching conference theme is, "From Fab Labs to Fab Cities," featuring Barcelona's unveiling of its road map for attaining self-sufficiency through digital fabrication in the years to come.

—**TOMAS DIEZ**, Director of Fab Lab Barcelona, FAB10 Barcelona conference co-chair, co-founder of Smart Citizen

FAB FOUNDATION

The Fab Foundation is an experiment in how to scale, support, and serve a globally distributed technical community. It began in 2009 to aid the rapid growth of the vibrant and culturally diverse fab lab network by providing some of the necessary connective tissue.

We have since evolved to become a foundation of foundations, supporting regional networks of fab labs as labs scale rapidly across continents and providing international services in areas such as finance, insurance, employment, education, communications, funding, and lab technical deployment. Recently, our nonprofit was awarded $10 million by Chevron Corporation to build and support labs across the USA.

The Fab Foundation is also seeking a Federal charter through the United States National Fab Lab Network Act, currently before Congress.

—**SHERRY LASSITER**, Director of the Fab Foundation, Program Manager Center for Bits and Atoms

FAB ACADEMY

Roughly equivalent to MIT's rapid prototyping course, MAS 863: How to Make (Almost) Anything, the Fab Academy provides advanced technical instruction through a unique, distributed, hands-on digital fabrication curriculum.

Professor Gershenfeld lectures globally through an interactive, two-way platform while experts mentor local student groups. Diploma completion is evaluated by a student's documented portfolio of skill-based projects rather than in time or credits.

If a 19-week prototyping marathon that tests your mettle as you and your classmates pull together to attempt every digital fabrication and electronics prototyping process possible in a fab lab sounds like fun (it is!) — join us next spring at a fab lab near you through fabacademy.org. ◉

—**ANNA KAZIUNAS FRANCE**, Fab Academy Dean of Students and Digital Fabrication Editor at Maker Media.

Elefab, a zip-tied, cardboard 3D puzzle elephant assembled at a Fab Kids workshop.

The Open Source Beehives evolved from John Rees' 2013 Fab Academy final project; a collaboration with Annemie Maes of OKNO and of Green Fab Lab's Jonathan Minchin.

"Hyperhabitat: Reprogramming the World", a 2008 IoT multiscale habitat installation by Guallart Architects, IAAC, The CBA and Bestiario.

FAB TIMELINE
Key moments in fab lab evolution.

»**1998** 1st MAS: 863 How to Make (Almost) Anything MIT Class

»**2001** Nat'l Science Foundation grant founds early fab lab educational outreach; IAAC inaugurated

»**2002** Experimental labs: Boston's Museum of Science, Vigyan Ashram in India

»**2003** 1st fab lab launched in Boston, followed by Costa Rica, Norway and Ghana, most future fab labs are self-funded

»**2005** Fab lab user group meeting "Fab1," Symposium on Digital Fabrication in Norway, "Fab2"

»**2006** Fab3: South Africa

»**2007** Fab Lab Barcelona founded, Fab4: Chicago

»**2008** Hyperhabitat: Reprogramming the World in Venice, AS220 Labs chartered

»**2009** Machine begin Making Machines/fab labs 2.0 begins, Fab Foundation incorporated

»**2009** Fab Academy program begins, Fab5: India

»**2010** Fab6: Netherlands, Fab Lab House built

»**2011** Fab7: Peru, MTM Snap, Haystack Lab realized

»**2012** Fab8: New Zealand, Fab Lab Kamakura organized

»**2013** S.1705: National Fab Lab Network Act introduced

»**2013** Fab9: Japan, PopFab

»**2014** Fab10 Barcelona

TURN CODES INTO THINGS

+SKILL BUILDER
Written by Matt Keeter

The Fab Boom Box, designed pre-kokopelli in the Fab Modules. It plays music off of a standard SD card, runs on a single 9V battery, and can be fabricated for under $100.

MATT KEETER studied engineering at Harvey Mudd College, then got his M.S. at the MIT Center for Bits and Atoms. In his day job, he's an electrical engineer at Formlabs. Outside of work, he creates unusual CAD systems, makes DIY electronics, volunteers at the MIT climbing wall, and goes out swing dancing.

Matt Keeter

FREE, OPEN-SOURCE, PYTHON SCRIPT-BASED PARAMETRIC CAD — BRED FOR CAM FROM THE VERY BEGINNING.

Basic shapes can be smoothly blended together for unusual effects.

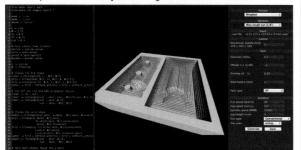

Currently, kokopelli CAM paths can be exported to Universal and Epilog laser cutters, the Roland Modela mini-mill, three- and five-axis Shopbot machines, and plain G-code. A modular workflow makes adding new machines easy.

KOKOPELLI AND ANTIMONY ARE PARAMETRIC, IMPERATIVE, IMPLICIT FRAMEWORKS for computer-aided design that grew out of my master's thesis at the MIT Center for Bits and Atoms and were tested in the Fab Academy and the Machines that Make MIT class. Currently, kokopelli is suitable for 2D and 3D modeling and PCB design. It can export .pngs, .svgs, and .stls, and there's basic built-in CAM for 2-, 3-, and 5-axis subtractive machining. Antimony, intended to be kokopelli's spiritual successor, is experimental and under active development.

LIKE OPENSCAD, WITH BUILT-IN CAM

These tools are built on an unusual solid modeling paradigm: Objects are represented as mathematical expressions, not as collections of polygons and edges (similar to OpenSCAD). This paradigm makes constructive solid geometry (e.g., unions, intersections, cutouts, blending) very easy. The downside is that some operations (like chamfering) become tricky to express.

If you get nervous when trigonometry starts showing its ugly face, don't panic! Understanding the underpinnings gives you more power to define your own shapes and transformations, but it's not mandatory.

It's completely possible to design with the standard library of shapes or use a graphical interface created by a more advanced user without ever touching the math expressions at the heart of the design format.

THE SOLVER

On top of this abstraction sits a geometry engine, coded in C and optimized for speed. It renders either height-maps or triangulated meshes, with support for dynamic remeshing as the user moves the camera around the scene.

DESIGNER-FRIENDLY PYTHON

Instead of drafting- or feature-based modeling, objects in kokopelli are designed as Python scripts. Many designers and creative coders are already familiar with Python, so the learning curve isn't quite as steep as a domain-specific language. In addition, users have access to all of their favorite Python libraries.

UI ELEMENTS: SLIDERS AND MORE!

Models can also be parameterized by sliders and other interactive UI elements in the view panel. This allows more experienced designers to make template models that can be customized by less experienced users.

ANTIMONY

Antimony uses the same foundation as kokopelli but combines Python scripting with graph-based composition (similar to the Grasshopper extension for Rhino). Designers can connect inputs and outputs into graphs representing operations on a set of primitives. ◉

OPENSCAD VS KOKOPELLI

PROGRAM	CAPABILITIES	CODEBASE	FILE FORMATS	BUILT-IN CAM
OPENSCAD	Constructive solid geometry and extrusion of 2D outlines.	Solver in C++ and other open libraries	Import/Export: DXF, STL, and OFF	NONE
KOKOPELLI	2D and 3D modeling and PCB design	Solver in C, Python CAD libraries	Export Only: pngs, .svgs, and .stls	2, 3 and 5-axis subtractive machining

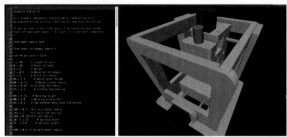

Inspired by Brett Victor's "Inventing on Principle." The left pane shows Python source code; the right pane shows the rendered model, which is updated in real time as the code changes.

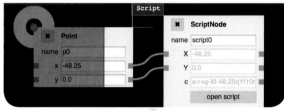

Antimony's scripting interface. Download from github.com/mkeeter/antimony

KOKOPELLI QUICKSTART: PARAMETRIC LIVING HINGE
By Anna Kaziunas France

 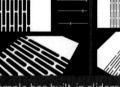

The kokopelli living hinge example has built-in sliders that make it simple to create your own bespoke flexibles from rigid materials using digital fabrication tools.

The Mac application and the Mac/Linux source (both at **github.com/mkeeter/kokopelli**) include examples with graphical interfaces. After installing, open "hinge.ko" from the kokopelli file menu.

Drag the sliders to modify the hinge attributes, then adjust the piece size and border thickness by dragging the nodes on the top right corner.

When creating your hinge, design for your materials, fabrication method, and desired flexibility. Densely packed small cuts create more flexibility but are only suited to laser cutting. If you are using a router, your smallest possible cut width is limited to your tool dimension. After configuring, export the file and fabricate it. If you're using fab lab machines or plain G-code, you can send the file directly from kokopelli.

More kokopelli living hinge tips and tricks at makezine.com/go/kokopelli Share it: #makeprojects

Original code by 2014 Fab Academy student Terence J. Fagan and improved by Matt Keeter. Red acrylic lamp customized using kokopelli and fabricated by Anna Kaziunas France.

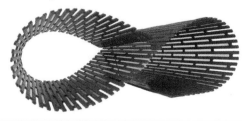

THE MOST INTERESTING MAKERSPACES IN AMERICA

WORKSHOPS COAST TO COAST ARE HELPING BUILDERS CONSTRUCT INCREDIBLE PROJECTS, BUT THE SPACES — AND THEIR MEMBERS — ARE OFTEN THE MOST NOTABLE CREATION.

WHAT MAKES A MAKERSPACE INTERESTING? It's not just the size of the shop or the number of active members. Nor is it the selection of tools or having an advanced RFID inventory system. Sure, those pieces count, but it's how a makerspace slots into its community —elevating and inspiring the makers — that makes it stand out.

We've compiled 34 shops across the country that keep our attention, from those that have revived historic industrial sites to libraries that offer access to the latest tool technologies. There are hundreds more around the country; to find one or details on how to start a makerspace near you, please visit makerspace.com and get connected.

Trammell Hudlon

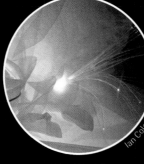

Ian Cole

Greg Richardson

Chad Elish

NYC RESISTOR
Brooklyn, New York
NYC Resistor claims some big-time founders, including Bre Pettis, but its chops also derive from a wonderful junk pile that members mine for odd parts. Home of the original MakerBot prototypes.

FAMILAB
Longwood, Florida
Near Orlando, Florida, 4,000-square-foot FamiLAB regularly gets global guests, who exchage ideas and inspiration. They also produce the Orlando Maker Faire and offer a slew of maker tools

7 HILLS
Rome, Georgia
Located in an old Masonic Lodge, 7 Hills is possibly the most beautiful makerspace to lounge or work, with murals featured on the walls and ceiling.

HACKPITTSBURGH
Pittsburgh, Philadelphia
Members here are inventors, artists, scientists, engineers, and more, who meet in a garage uptown.

Mary Barnett

Yale Center for Engineering Innovation & Design

FOURTH FLOOR
CHATTANOOGA PUBLIC LIBRARY
Chattanooga, Tennessee
It's literally the 4th floor of the Chattanooga Public Library, where the focus isn't on consuming knowledge but creating it, using high- and low-tech tools, and the space is open to anyone with a library card.

NOVA LABS, INC
Reston, Virginia
This space features giant lasers, a beautiful woodshop, and a 1940s jukebox which streams Pandora.

Nova Labs

YALE CENTER FOR ENGINEERING INNOVATION AND DESIGN
New Haven, Connecticut
Engineers Without Borders, HackYale, and iGEM — the International Genetically Engineered Machine Foundation — are just a few of the student groups that use this campus space.

Keith Simmonl

ARTISAN'S ASYLUM
Somerville, Massachusetts
Artisan's Asylum is one of the largest makerspaces in the country. Housed in the old Ames Safety Envelope facility, this village of 120 makers' studios under one roof comes with fabrication tools galore and offers classes for new makers on everything from bike building to lampworking. Don't miss Stompy, their Kickstarted giant hexapod robot (see page 49).

Ellen Jorgensen

GENSPACE
Brooklyn, New York
Genspace is a biolab, offering biotechnology education to adults and children, as well as opportunities for innovation and entrepreneurship.

EAST

R. Kelley Marchat of Merlin Productions.

THE COLUMBUS IDEA FOUNDRY
Columbus, Ohio

This massive makerspace — around 75,000 square feet, including a new rooftop addition — is thoroughly integrated in its community, partnering with the nonprofit Community Development Corporation, the Center of Science and Industry, and the 400 West Rich arts facility. All occur within two blocks of each other in a re-emerging neighborhood, and the Foundry is already showing its influence; a handheld scanner company that got its start there has leased space in the neighborhood as well.

Kelly Murphy

THE HACK FACTORY
Minneapolis, Minnesota

Minnesota's largest member-owned, multiple-discipline shop features a cabinetry-quality wood shop, a welding studio, and a machine shop, but it's most famous for its life-size game of Operation.

Tim Bruening

LORAIN COUNTY COMMUNITY COLLEGE
Elyria, Ohio

See the shop that President Obama visited and the CNC-milled sign that welcomed him.

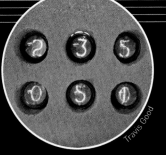
Travis Good

ARCH REACTOR
St. Louis, Missouri

Electronics-heavy shop with an incredible roof-deck bar and view of the arch.

Omaha Maker Group

OMAHA MAKER GROUP
Omaha, Nebraska

Affectionately known as OMG, this space grew from a bakery basement ("The Makery") into a 40-member shop that will help host Omaha's first Mini Maker Faire.

Daniel Simser

BOZEMAN MAKERSPACE
Bozeman, Montana

A small but growing space in a building that used to house livestock auctions.

Benjamin Groves

DALLAS MAKERSPACE
Dallas, Texas

This community workshop also focuses on science lab work and art, and especially collaborative projects.

Jeff Cicolani

ATX HACKERSPACE CO-OP
Austin, Texas

ATX was the first hackerspace in Austin and, with 8,000 square feet and 180 members, is one of the largest in Texas. With full metal and wood shops, it houses electric car conversions, a 60-watt Universal laser cutter, and acts as a practice space for Arc Attack, the Tesla-coil band. Recent projects include "Alfred" the tool-retrieval robot and a colossal projection-mapped hexahedron sculpture.

Rodolfo Parisi - www.drivius.net

LAWRENCE CREATES
Lawrence, Kansas

Among other projects, this makerspace is home to a group of neuropsychology enthusiasts who are working on consciousness visualizations.

Eric Ose

HEATSYNC LABS
Mesa, Arizona

Home of Joey "Marshmallow Canon" Hudy and your typical scanning electron microscope hack; it's free and open to the public, sustained by community donations.

Pete Prodoehl

MILWAUKEE MAKERSPACE
Milwaukee, Wisconsin

Milwaukee Makerspace offers detailed online tutorials for much of its equipment; they also house an active electric vehicle club.

David Lewinski

I3 DETROIT
Detroit, Michigan

Their extensive list of tools and equipment makes this one of the most established and well-known spaces around.

CPL Staff

TECHCENTRAL
Cleveland, Ohio

The Cleveland Public Library moved its DVD library to make room for 3D printers, a laser cutter, kits, and collaboration space.

Mike Warot

PUMPING STATION: ONE
Chicago, Illinois

Beer brewing is one of the staples here, alongside fabrication and wood and metal working.

LVL 1 Hackerspace

LVL1 HACKERSPACE
Louisville, Kentucky

Democratic roots run strong through the 8,000-square-foot LVL1, which started a "makerships" program for makers who can't afford memberships.

Quelab

QUELAB
Albuquerque, New Mexico

Famous for their interactive starship bridge, a four-headed 3D printer designed there, and the 80-watt laser cutter/engraver in their 6,800-foot space.

GREAT LAKES CENTRAL

Beatrice Murch

THE CRUCIBLE
Oakland, California
A vast, well-equipped space for learning fine and industrial arts, from blacksmithing to glass blowing to jewelry to stone work.

Shears Adkins Rockmore Architects

ADX
Portland, Oregon
ADX is one of a growing number of makerspaces that'll do the making for you; their Custom Design & Fabrication team helps design and build projects for clients. Of course, you can still build stuff yourself.

DeLaMare Library

DELAMARE LIBRARY, UNIV. OF NEVADA, RENO
Reno, Nevada
Lockpicking kits, 3D scanning and printing, and Arduino prototyping are available to all in UN-Reno's science and engineering library.

Mitch Altman

NOISEBRIDGE
San Francisco, California
A diverse space founded in 2007 that hosts a monthly series of lightning talks, called "Five Minutes of Fame," where members give lectures on a wide variety of topics.

BIOCURIOUS
Sunnyvale, California
Originally a cooperative lab in a Silicon Valley garage, BioCurious grew into a member-based makerspace for biologists, complete with wet lab and biosafety certification. Instead of laser cutters and 3D printers, BioCurious offers centrifuges and polymerase chain reaction machines. The nonprofit is one of a growing class of biohacking spaces that are making real science experiments possible, offering classes and workshops as well as encouraging community projects, where members and nonmembers work together on research and experiments.

Patrik D'haeseleer

Amelia Greenhall

DOUBLE UNION
San Francisco, California
A makerspace for women, in a comfortable, welcoming, and high-tech environment.

Gene Sherman

VOCADEMY
Riverside, California
All the right stuff, plus a commitment to bring industrial arts education back to schools.

Ace Monster Toys

ACE MONSTER TOYS
Oakland, California
A giant laser, tools galore, and lots of LED signs are tucked away in this warehouse, which includes programs for kids.

David Schellema

AUTODESK PIER 9
San Francisco, California
Pier 9 belongs to Autodesk, and the company spared no expense building the ultimate makerspace. It has every tool a maker could want, but it's open only to Autodesk employees and artists in residence.

WEST

SNAP SHOT

A PEEK INSIDE SECTOR67, MADISON, WI

HOME OF THE THREE-TIME POWER RACING SERIES CHAMPIONS, SECTOR67 is a well-organized hackerspace near the state capitol in Madison, Wisconsin. The nonprofit was bootstrapped by Chris Meyer, the sole founder and benevolent dictator who launched it after taking a $7,000 second prize in a business plan competition. That's not a lot of money for tools, so Meyer and Sector67's members began rebuilding and refurbishing well-used (and sometimes broken) equipment, from CNC mills and routers to injection equipment and sewing machines. The nine shots here show just a bit of what's inside their 8,500-square-foot space. ⊘

Riley Wilkinson

1

2

3

1. Cast iron, like this Valentine's Day pour and Minecraft pickaxe, is a big facet of Sector67.

2. Unsorted hardware is just junk in a box. These drawers hold lots of old-school electronics stock.

3. A well-used third hand, handmade from a block of wood, screw, washer, steel wire, and alligator clips.

4. Sector67's Chris Meyer works their manual milling machine.

5. Another cast-iron creation, this metal head was made from a 3D Kinect scan, sliced up into a laser-cutter file in 123D Make.

6. A 1980s Melco embroidery machine that has been converted to USB using an Arduino to emulate the output of the original paper tape reader.

7. Milled injection molds for Sector67 poker chips.

8. Cleverly crafted shelves use dowels rather than a solid platform to hold only plastic shoeboxes, helping keep Sector67's materials organized.

9. Meyer in the wood shop, where Sector67 keeps a Jet 12" planer/joiner, a Grizzly drum/flap sander, a Stinger CNC router, and racks of lumber, boards and other build materials.

4

5

6

7

8

9

INDUSTRIAL INSTRUMENTS

SOMETIMES THE RIGHT TOOL FOR THE JOB CAN'T BE FOUND AT HOME.

Written by Stuart Deutsch

FACE IT, YOU MAY NEVER HAVE ALL THE TOOLS YOU WANT OR NEED. Some may be too big and heavy to fit inside your home or workspace, others too expensive or infrequently needed to make sense.

Makerspaces, however, give makers access to those less-than-convenient tools to build projects that might otherwise be impossible. Expect some or all of the following tools at a makerspace, but be prepared for the learning curve for handling more complex ones.

KEY: DEGREE OF DIFFICULTY

1: Learn on your own

2: Quick intro or expert guidance recommended

3: Training session required

4: Training and practice recommended

5: More training and practice is required

STUART DEUTSCH is the founder of ToolGuyd (ToolGuyd.com), a source for tool reviews and recommendations.

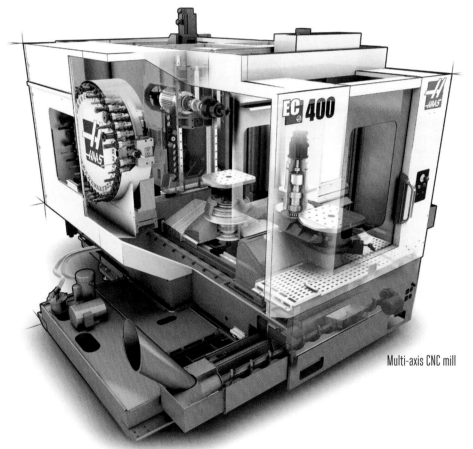

Multi-axis CNC mill

MULTI-AXIS AND LARGE CNC MILLS AND ROUTERS

Four- and 5-axis CNC machines allow you to fabricate parts that you can't create any other way. The expanded capabilities translate to greater machine complexity, size, and costs, however, which can be restrictive for all but the largest makerspaces.

Full-size CNC routers, like those with a bed size of 96"×48" or larger, allow you to carve full-size sheets of plywood, MDF, OSB, foam, and other sheet materials.

◊ **PRO TIP:** If your machine doesn't have a vacuum table, buy or build one — this will save you a lot of time and effort.
◊ **BRANDS:** ShopBot (multi-axis router, large routers), HAAS (multi-axis CNC)
◊ **DIFFICULTY:** 3 (router), 5 (multi-axis CNC)

LASER, WATERJET, AND PLASMA CNC CUTTERS

These powerful cutting tools create precise 2D shapes from sheet materials. Most makerspaces buy a laser cutter first, as lasers can be used on thin acrylic, wood, and other sheet materials, even fabric. Plasma tends to be the next step as makers move into cutting sheet metal, while waterjet cutters are mainly found in the more well-outfitted spaces.

◊ **PRO TIP:** Waterjet cutters don't have the warping and work-hardening issues that laser and plasma cutters have, and they leave a clean, burr-free cut.
◊ **BRANDS:** Epilog (lasers), Jet Edge (waterjet)
◊ **DIFFICULTY:** 2 (laser), 3 (others)

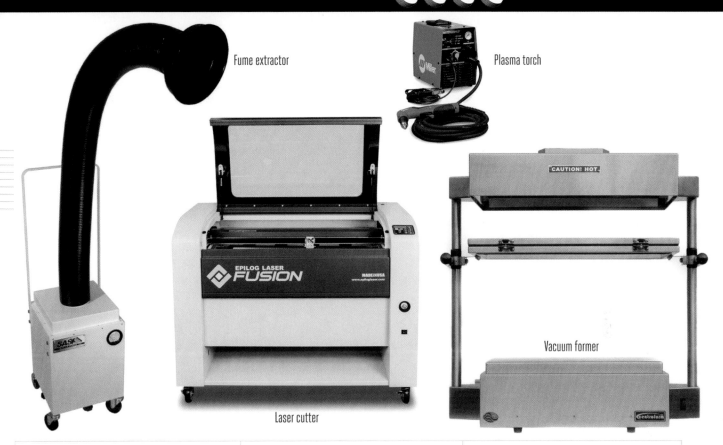

Fume extractor

Plasma torch

Laser cutter

Vacuum former

WELDING AND HANDHELD PLASMA CUTTING EQUIPMENT

Welding steel and other metals opens makers to new possibilities, like customizing heavy-duty jigs, frames, and chassis.

◇ **PRO TIP:** Once you're comfortable with MIG, start exploring gas-torch welding for the artsy stuff and TIG welding for the high tech stuff.
◇ **BRANDS:** Lincoln Electric, Miller
◇ **DIFFICULTY:** 4

VAPOR AND FUME CONTAINMENT

Certain operations, like laser cutting, spray painting, or mixing resins and chemicals, require strict vapor and fume containment or control. While painting booths, fume hoods, and even UV biosafety cabinets can be affordable to build or buy, they require a space commitment. Portable fume extractors, dust collectors, and air cleaners are good options for those with smaller spaces.

◇ **PRO TIP:** Make yourself a paint booth. The quality of your paint jobs will drastically improve.
◇ **BRANDS:** Hakko (portable fume extractor), Sentry Air (hoods and extraction systems)
◇ **DIFFICULTY:** 2

INDUSTRIAL MACHINERY

Industrial equipment such as drill presses, lathes, band saws, hydraulic presses, sanders, grinders, and other such tools can save a lot of time and produce better results than hand tools or improvised jigs. However, while many makers and makerspaces focus time and money on CNC tools and cutters, they sometimes forget that several manual operations, such as deburring a saw-cut edge, are far easier to do with simpler equipment.

◇ **PRO TIP:** Learning to do everything by hand first helps you find the easiest and most cost effective way of doing things — you don't always need a CNC machine to drill a straight hole.
◇ **BRANDS:** Grizzly, Enco
◇ **DIFFICULTY:** 3

METAL-FORMING TOOLS

Complex three-dimensional shapes can be crafted from ordinary sheet metal. Thin-gauge aluminum, steel, and nonferrous metals can be easily cut and formed using hand tools, but thicker or larger pieces of sheet metal are better worked on full-size equipment.

Pan and box brakes, shears, slip rolls, punches, notchers, shrinkers, stretchers, English wheels, planishing hammers, and bead rollers are among the most common tools metalworkers use to work their magic.

◇ **PRO TIP:** If you get good enough at shaping sheet metal into complex curves, you can score high paying jobs in custom auto body shops.
◇ **BRANDS:** Tennsmith, Grizzly
◇ **DIFFICULTY:** 2

LARGE AIR COMPRESSOR AND PNEUMATIC EQUIPMENT

Simply adding a large-capacity air compressor to a makerspace expands the scope of equipment that can be used. Some tools, such as bead blasters and paint sprayers, require constant pressurized air sources, as do the subsystems of other types of machinery, including CNC mills. Other air tools, such as grinders and sanders, are often significantly smaller than AC-powered ones, but you have to deal with managing an air hose.

◇ **PRO TIP:** You can never have an air compressor that is too big.
◇ **BRANDS:** Ingersoll Rand, Rolair
◇ **DIFFICULTY:** 2

HIGH TEMPERATURE EQUIPMENT

Larger makerspaces may have heating equipment like furnaces, ovens, and specialty tools such as acrylic sheet benders and vacuum formers, allowing makers to do things like blow glass or bend or form plastic sheets into complex shapes.

◇ **BRANDS:** Delvie's Plastics Inc. (Strip heater), Centroform (Vacuum former)
◇ **DIFFICULTY:** 2

TEXTILES AND SEWING TOOLS

A well-equipped makerspace should contain a sewing machine at the very least, especially as the trend of wearable projects has surged recently, and a serger is handy for edgework, hemming, and seaming. A vinyl cutter can also be used to create silk-screen stencils.

◇ **BRANDS:** Singer, Juki
◇ **DIFFICULTY:** 1

MAKERSPACE TO MARKET

A GOOD COMMUNITY MAKES GOING PRO EASIER THAN EVER.

Written by Travis Good

Synthetos

Adam Ellsworth

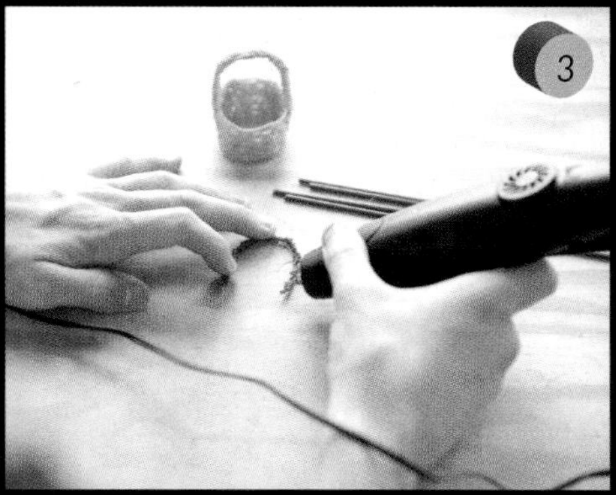

Jeffrey Braverman

DIYSect

Nova Labs

MAKERSPACES AREN'T JUST A SOURCE OF CAMARADERIE AND HOBBY-LEVEL ONE-OFF PROJECTS. They also occasionally create and manufacture pro-level consumer products and services. Here are a few notable items that you can purchase, which have come from makerspaces around the country.

1. QUESTION BLOCK LAMP

Adam Ellsworth and Bryan Duxbury developed and prototyped this Mario-inspired lamp at TechShop San Francisco. After posting on Etsy, they received huge blog attention and sold 300 lamps immediately. They then enlisted a crack team from within TechShop and manually made over 1000 lamps. The next year, they launched a Kickstarter and raised $131,000 to scale up production. The additional lamps sold out; Adam and Bryan are now busy producing more.

2. TINYG

Alden Hart met his partner Riley Porter at HackDC, and together they built the TinyG. The six-axis CNC controller with 4 motor outputs continues to get great reviews for its ability to outperform existing CNC and 3D printer controllers. Members of HackDC were early users and a regular source of feedback. The board is now available through the Maker Shed, Inventables, Adafruit, and Tiny G's parent company, Synthetos. They're also embedded in a variety of products including the Othermill and the 5-axis PocketNC.

3. 3DOODLER

Artisan's Asylum has a community of makers under its roof who work, dream, and collaborate. Out of this alchemy came the 3Doodler, a 3D-printing pen by Pete Dilworth and Max Bogue, which made its way to a record-setting

BIZARRO BUILDS

Written by Mike Senese

Kickstarter of $2.3 million. Now their invention is shipping worldwide and is even available at the Museum of Modern Art.

4. THE GLOWING PLANT

"Natural lighting" took on new meaning when this team, led by Kyle Taylor, designed glow-in-the-dark plants. Needing a wet lab, they collaborated in the pioneering bio hackerspace, BioCurious, in 2012. From there it was a short leap to a Kickstarter, where it rocketed past its goal by bringing in almost half a million dollars.

5. SMALL BATCH ASSEMBLY

Makerspaces also hatch service businesses. The Nova Labs makerspace is home to this company that provides low-volume electronics assembly services specifically for makers, making it one of few makerspace co-located with a production-grade pick-and-place machine and reflow oven. This close proximity has continuously spawned synergies and projects including a Nova Labs-branded Arduino-compatible development board. ◯

TRAVIS GOOD

is currently focusing on the transformative potential of the maker movement in libraries, science museums, schools, and civic government. He has visited 28 incubators, 100+ makerspaces, and multiple fab labs while also chairing a start-up incubator and co-founding a makerspace in Virginia. He also co-founded and produced the Hardware Innovation Workshop, MakerCon, and San Diego Mini Maker Faire. His broader agenda is available at make.GoodPursuits.com.

Artisan's Asylum.

ANYTHING IS POSSIBLE WITH THE RIGHT MIX OF BRAINS AND BRAWN. And we all know that when we get together with our best buds, things often take a hilarious turn towards the ludicrous. Some of the oversized, outlandish projects coming out of makerspaces prove just how true — and fun — that is.

STOMPY THE HEXAPOD

One of the flagship projects at Artisan's Asylum, this two-ton, six-legged metal beast will be able to carry two riders above its 18' footprint, through almost any type of terrain. Kickstarted to the tune of nearly $100,000, construction is underway.

WORLD'S LARGEST VENDING MACHINE

For the 2014 SXSW music festival, North Street Labs, based in Portsmouth, Virginia, designed and built this six-story interactive stage installation to hold 800 bags of Doritos (the full-size variety). An equivalent number of custom release pegs, controlled by an array of Arduino and Raspberry Pi boards, dropped the snacks to hungry attendees through tweeted commands.

North Street Labs

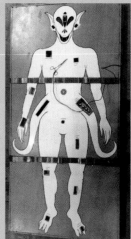

LVL1

ALIEN AUTOPSY

Louisville's LVL1 Hackerspace created this knockoff of the classic home game Operation, but to a much larger scale and with an extraterrestrial twist. The 3'x6' space-alien board uses hemostats connected to buzzer circuits to sound an alarm if an amateur pathologist incorrectly removes any of the internals from the specimen chambers.

KICKING GAS

Written by Jack Hegenauer

AN ENERGY-THRIFTY ELECTRIC VEHICLE CONVERSION IS THE PERFECT COLLABORATION.

Electric Minor Project

DNO 172G

JACK HEGENAUER
A native of Michigan, Jack has a Ph.D. in biochemistry and did research at UC San Diego for 25 years. He managed corporate research in health sciences for many years before retiring in San Diego, where he spends his time working to improve air quality and to master EV technology.

Kick Gas Car Club

EVEN AS COMMERCIAL EV'S BECOME MORE WIDELY AVAILABLE, DEDICATED PODS OF CAR ENTHUSIASTS AND DIY HOBBYISTS CONTINUE TO ENJOY MAKING OLDER TRUCKS, CARS, OR MOTORCYCLES RUN EXCLUSIVELY ON ELECTRONS. In San Diego, several novices got together in 2007 to convert personal autos in the home garage of local guru Abrán Quevedo, a former auto mechanic and high school shop teacher. Later, we organized ourselves into a collective — the Kick Gas Car Club — that shares tools, hard-won expertise, fellowship, outreach, and a more spacious workshop in a rented hangar at a local airfield. Here are a few lessons from our experience if you're thinking about "kicking gas."

BEFORE YOU BEGIN
Think hard about whether you have the time, energy, space, and — especially — the money to complete your project. An effective conversion can cost from $12,000 to $18,000, depending on the power and driving

range you anticipate. Do you have the mechanical expertise, tools, equipment, guidance, and friends to help where needed? Do you have access to a makerspace where you can learn to machine or weld the various brackets and widgets that are inevitably required?

THE DONOR CAR

The best conversions are small, lightweight, older cars that you can buy on the cheap. (Look for something with a blown engine, since you'll be ditching it anyway.) It should have good working brakes and an intact electrical/computer system, essential for air bags, etc. A manual transmission makes by far the easiest conversion. Also, plan to beef up the suspension — even though you will be removing the engine, exhaust train, and fuel system, the battery pack and other components will add weight. Power brakes and power steering are highly desirable but can be retrofit with aftermarket kits.

THE BATTERIES ... LEAD OR LITHIUM?

Conversions have traditionally used readily available flooded lead-acid, deep-cycle golf cart batteries, but these are heavy and messy compared to the new generation of lighter, more compact — and more expensive — lithium batteries that offer greater power density. Enough batteries of identical voltage and capacity (measured in ampere-hours, Ah) must be connected in series using heavy copper cables or bus bars to supply the voltages required by the particular motor that you have selected. (A typical "propulsion pack" for a DC motor would supply 144V.)

THE BATTERY BOX

Even lithium batteries are still heavy enough to require secure restraints in case of accidental collision. Ideally, all batteries should be contained in a welded steel box that's secured to the car's frame, and clamped down tightly to prevent movement. Heavier flooded lead-acid batteries pose the additional hazards of spillage and production of potentially flammable gases during charging, so a battery box should be designed with a tight lid that allows venting.

THE MOTOR

Batteries are DC, so 9- to 11-inch DC motors have traditionally been used. AC motors, however, are growing in popularity; they offer some size advantages but are more electronically complex.

Both require a carefully machined adapter plate to couple them to the clutch and transmission. If you have access to a CNC lathe, you can find specs for a variety of transmissions online. You will have to adapt the old engine mounts to support the heavy new motor.

THE MOTOR (SPEED) CONTROLLER

These are the costliest items in any conversion. Motor speed is controlled electronically using MOSFETs to supply pulse-width modulation of battery current at a constant voltage. Pack voltages of 140V–300V are common, and motors may draw up to 1,000A, so considerable heat can be generated in the electronics. Modern controllers are water-cooled, and many can be programmed for peak performance and safety through a CAN bus.

NOTE: THE CONTROLLER MUST MATCH THE VOLTAGE SUPPLIED BY THE PROPULSION PACK, SO DECISIONS ABOUT MOTOR, CONTROLLER, AND BATTERIES MUST BE MADE TOGETHER.

THE BATTERY CHARGER

A battery charger is typically mounted onboard to allow recharging of the propulsion pack at any location with 110V or 220V AC power, such as your garage or an EV charging kiosk. A good charger will be programmable or preprogrammed to accommodate the specific battery chemistry (lead-acid or lithium) in your pack.

THE DC/DC CONVERTER

EVs lack an alternator to charge the 12V battery that powers the low-voltage control system, monitoring gauges, computer, headlights, radio, and wipers when the car is running. The alternator is replaced by an electronic switching power supply that converts the 100+V from the battery pack into 12V–14V to supply the voltage and current draw demanded by these systems, as well as to recharge the auxiliary battery.

The results of an EV conversion can be highly satisfying, especially if you've been able to turn a scrap car into something cool. Compared to the average internal-combustion engine, all-electric drives are smooth, quiet, and energy-efficient. All of us in the Kick Gas Club feel the heightened satisfaction of using these sophisticated technologies in a very fundamental way — where the rubber meets the road. ◓

Time Required:
Weeks to Months
Cost:
$12,000–$18,000

Tools
- » Hydraulic car lift or heavy car jack
- » Engine hoist
- » MIG wire welder and welding helmet
- » Band saw
- » Bench and hand grinders
- » Drill press and high-quality bits
- » Portable hand drill
- » Complete socket sets: ³/₈" and ½", SAE and metric
- » Torque wrench
- » Battery lug crimper for 2/0 – 4/0 copper welding cable
- » High-quality digital voltmeter/circuit tester/continuity meter
- » Battery chargers
- » Battery, lead-acid, 6V, 8V, or 12V
- » Battery packs, lead or lithium, 144V or greater
- » Battery discharge units (for "bottom balancing")
- » Battery capacity monitors ("coulomb counters") to track pack charge and discharge cycles
- » Small-gauge wiring hardware
- » Wire various gauges and colors
- » Crimping tool
- » Wire stripper
- » Soldering gun and solder
- » Wire lugs, connectors, quick disconnects
- » Heat-shrink tubing various sizes and colors
- » Heat gun
- » One big hammer
- » Many pots of coffee

WHERE ARE THE WOMEN?

Written by Georgia Guthrie

INSIGHTS INTO THE LACK OF FEMALE MAKERSPACE MEMBERS AND WHAT CAN BE DONE ABOUT IT.

Corinne Warnshuis

GEORGIA GUTHRIE is an artist, designer, and maker. She is the director of The Hacktory (thehacktory.org) and was named Philly's "Hacker of the Year" by the blog Geekadelphia. Georgia also works as a designer at the Action Mill.

IF YOU'VE BEEN TO YOUR LOCAL HACKER/MAKERSPACE AND NOTICED THERE WEREN'T MANY WOMEN, did you stop to wonder why? Unfortunately a common reaction is to think, "I guess women just aren't into hacking or building stuff." As one of the few female directors of a U.S. makerspace, I know this just isn't true. Here's my perspective on the problem and what can be done about it.

When I was nominated to be director of The Hacktory, I decided to give it a try in an attempt to make the organization as inclusive as possible. Today The Hacktory, based in Philadelphia, has a pool of volunteers and organizers that is close to 50/50 men and women, tilting more towards women.

Frustrated with conversations about the gender gap that we witnessed at many tech conferences, we decided to take a deeper look at the issue. We designed a brief presentation and a workshop we call "Hacking the Gender Gap," where participants share positive and negative experiences they've had with technology. All the experiences are written on large Post-its, and placed on a timeline delineating relative age. The workshop concludes with a group analysis and discussion of where the positive and negative experiences cluster, and other emergent themes. The stories provide an incredibly rich context in which to understand how the gender gap is experienced in day-to-day life.

In the age range from birth to 10 years, many positive stories involve doing a tech-oriented activity with a parent, like learning to program or working with power tools. Another theme is a family member purchasing a computer or video game system, which participants use to build websites or gain confidence in their skills.

In the teen years, negative stories of teachers, guidance counselors, or other advisors discouraging girls' interests or questioning their abilities in STEM subjects are frequent. Some comments seem unintentional, like a tutor saying, "I don't know why this is so difficult for you — it's so easy." Others are brutal, like a female chemistry teacher with a Ph.D. telling students, "Women are bad at science."

Before designing this workshop, our team thought these kinds of experiences were in the distant past, but we've gathered many stories that occurred five years ago or less.

When reading through the stories, women often say, "I thought it was just me!" Many participants express relief and thanks for the chance to share their experiences — both positive and negative — in a non-judgmental environment, and have those experiences contribute to a larger outcome.

The results became more interesting with mixed-gender crowds. One crucial theme that emerged from the men's stories was frustration with women asking for help with a technical problem, following the assumption that men can fix it just because they're male. These stories helped us understand how our culture's association of masculinity with technical ability can be perpetuated by all genders.

In our research, we found the 2002 study "Women in Computing Around the World," which details how other countries don't have the same gender gap in STEM interests or careers. Female students in China have shown to be much more confident in their abilities with computers than male students. In Thailand, Italy, and Kenya, men were significantly more anxious than women about using technology.

Our most significant takeaways from doing this workshop include:

» Gender gap research in the U.S. lacks context. Recent studies seek to identify the age when girls "lose interest" in STEM fields, rather than the experiences that contribute to that shift.
» Women experience direct and indirect discouragement from teachers, guidance counselors, and tutors, something most men never experience.
» The gender gap is perpetuated by all genders, adding to its pervasiveness.
» Supportive or discouraging comments stay with people for years.

So what can a hacker/makerspace do to encourage women to start participating in their space and retain them? A good first step is to question the assumptions and biases present in your space. When

a woman walks through your door, is the general assumption that she must be a beginner or that she's tagging along with someone else? Such assumptions may be based in real experiences, but to address this problem, lay these experiences aside.

There's something called "Imposter Syndrome," which is a constant comparing and questioning of one's own abilities to those of others, and a fear that you'll be revealed to not know as much as you claim. Women in science and tech fields experience this self-doubt at a very high rate, often halting them from revealing the skills and understanding they possess.

If your space has several women, including women in leadership positions, you're in good shape. To grow and empower this

"A good first step is to question the assumptions and biases present in your makerspace."

group, consider the following.

Conduct an anonymous survey about what's working and not working for the women in your space. A lot of women won't voice issues to not rock the boat or because they just don't have the energy and are willing to put up with irritating conditions.

From the issues they raise, ask them to prioritize three things to address with immediate action without a vote from the larger group. A vote is exactly how the existing way of doing things will continue to reinforce itself, without allowing the concerns of this minority to be addressed.

Provide visual cues for women to show them they're welcome. This could include a designated greeter for your open house

who wears a special pin or name tag. Other cues could include a well-thought-out and enforceable conflict resolution or "no jerks" policy displayed prominently in your space.

Hold open shop time or design classes for artists, crafters, or creatives. More women are comfortable identifying as these titles rather than as hackers or programmers. Many spaces have found success with offering classes for "women and their friends." This could be a good way to get more women to set foot in your space. Naturally, it would be ideal for a woman to take the lead in organizing such events.

If your hacker/makerspace has no women or just one, unfortunately it may be difficult to change. Evaluate if the regulars feel that the lack of diversity is something that "just happened" or a big problem. If the former attitude prevails, this group may view the tech world as a meritocracy and may reject the idea that the forces of culture and stereotype hold women back. Without the understanding that the urge to explore science, technology, and physics is an innately human thing, this group may not be able to suspend their judgment and make the changes necessary to attract women and other minority groups.

Rather than trying to change this underlying perception, find others in your community who share the value of inclusion, and start your own space. The time you invest in growing this space will pay off much faster than you imagine. ◔

The Hacktory

TECHSHOP'S NOT-SO-SECRET INGREDIENT

Written by Nathan Hurst

TO ACHIEVE ITS PRODIGIOUS GOALS, THE MARQUEE MAKERSPACE IS DIALING IN A PRECISE METHOD TO MAKE EACH NEW SHOP POLISHED AND PROFITABLE.

TechShop
BUILD YOUR DREAMS HERE

1

2

Jeffrey Braverman

JIM NEWTON TALKS ABOUT THE HIGH-POWERED EQUIPMENT AT TECHSHOP like a car geek talks about fuel injection, horsepower, and torque. Many terms are even the same; as he walks past a Jet vertical milling machine, he mentions its 3-horsepower motor, variable speed, and digital display.

Newton is the founder of TechShop, the (arguably) first and (almost certainly) most well-defined makerspace. At 18,000 square feet, their flagship San Francisco shop is filled with his favorite tools and equipment.

He loves the Tin Knocker hand turret punch for its precision and the clean holes it creates, the cold saw (also from Jet) because he always wanted one but could never justify buying it for himself. He calls the manual lathe "one of the workhorses of the industrial revolution." All these tools — including 3D printers and laser cutters — add up to a big part of what makes TechShop TechShop.

The company stands out among makerspaces, while the "makerspace" category itself remains somewhat ill defined. TechShop tends to be the Platonic ideal. That's not to call it generic; it's simply come closest to defining the category, partly because of its standardization and partly because of its scope. With eight stores in strategic U.S. maker markets, they're the biggest membership-model shop around.

Still, TechShop has bigger plans. According to CEO Mark Hatch, it intends to scale up to between 60 and 100 locations around North America, essentially growing by around a factor of 10. To do so, it will need to depend on a fairly strict set of parameters and methods that will go into every new location, sort of a "TechShop protocol."

Hatch and the TechShop crew aren't secretive about it. He doesn't see much in the way of competitors because he doesn't think others can do the same — it's just too expensive. "It comes down to capital, and these are very capital-intensive businesses," he says. "It's hard. It's expensive. The price points are pretty low at $125 a month. This is not an easy business by any stretch of the imagination." Each shop, he says, costs between $2.5 and $3.5 million to open.

The newest one, in Arlington, Virginia, passed the 500-member mark prior to opening in June, with an additional 3,000 free memberships for veterans in a partnership with the Department of Veterans Affairs Center for Innovation. He partly attributes that success to a campaign that signed up 200 members before its April soft opening.

TechShop has a history of promising big things. The early promotion of the Arlington shop helped sell those memberships, but in a few towns it backfired. A franchising experiment went awry, and shops in Portland, Oregon and Raleigh-Durham, North Carolina closed, while one in Brooklyn has been in the works for three years without getting off the ground.

To Hatch, those are simply growing pains. They just need to stick to the protocol and adapt it to handle new challenges. The company no longer licenses franchise deals. Newton notes that the Portland and Raleigh shops were opened when they had just one location (in Menlo Park, California). "We didn't really know how we were

"IT'S QUITE A BIT DIFFERENT FROM A SMALL BUSINESS OPERATION. YOU HAVE DOZENS OF PEOPLE USING A TOOL, AND THEY'RE ALL USING IT IN DIFFERENT WAYS."

1. At TechShop San Francisco, 3D printers are housed on a quiet top level.

2. The company offers from 100 to 200 classes per month, like this one in the woodshop, from introductory to advanced.

3. A member works in the electronics lab.

4. TechShop designed and built all the elements in its lobby.

5

even running that one. I couldn't hand someone a franchise book and say, 'Here's how you operate a TechShop and make it profitable,'" he says. "What we told these guys was ... 'look at TechShop Menlo Park, figure out how it works, and you need to replicate it yourself.'"

Ultimately, Newton blames the location choices — neither the Portland nor Raleigh shop was near an urban center. Location is now essential in their protocol; each new shop should be situated where people want to be, near restaurants and bars and transportation.

That's a contrast to many grassroots maker-spaces, points out Peter Hirshberg, chairman of the Re:Imagine Group and the Gray Area Foundation for the Arts. Makerspaces based on activities like machining and welding are often in industrial areas where they can take up space, says Hirshberg. "TechShop, on the other hand, is this new form of advanced manufacturing that doesn't need such a big space."

The company learned one other lesson from Portland: All new locations must feature brand new equipment.

Equipment is still probably the biggest single aspect of the company's protocol. TechShop's website has a list of core tools and equipment, and they don't vary much from location to location — down to the machines' brands and model numbers. This allows them to standardize train-

ing, repairs, and safety, and members can walk in and use equipment at any location, thanks to an RFID tag in their badges.

John Taylor, who helped with TechShop's national rollout, fought to standardize the list. He worked with architects to customize the locations, pointing out that the electrical engineers needed that information to correctly design the circuits and outlets. "Dealing with layout was a constant battle of trade-offs," he adds. "Executives wanted big open sight-lines, while those with a maker background expressed the need for walls, vertical storage, and partitioned program areas."

The San Francisco location compromised the two, and it's the only multilevel TechShop. On the top floor are quieter, cleaner tools like laser cutters and 3D printers, as well as a lounge area and a bank of computers loaded with company partner Autodesk's software. Below, on a split-level, a conference room with a glass wall overlooks the machine shop, where the vertical mills and hand punch live alongside a 60,000-psi Flow Jet water jet and a big, red and black Lincoln Electric ventilation system that clings to the east wall like a spider. A wood shop is set to the side, with four walls and a wide entryway emanating the whine of saws and the smell of sawdust, though a humming dust collector and air-filtration system keeps much of it from es-

"THERE'S MAGIC THAT HAPPENS AROUND THE COMMUNITY ASPECT. THEY WANT TO SEE THEIR FRIENDS, THEY WANT TO HANG OUT A LITTLE BIT LONGER."

5. In addition to 3D printers, the top floor incorporates laser cutters, a lounge with coffee and vending machines, and a bank of computers tricked out with Autodesk software.

6. Band saw practice in the woodshop.

7. The back entrance is oversized to allow large projects and materials. Beside it, a powder-coating station is big enough for a motorcycle body.

caping into the rest of the shop.

In the woodshop are two ShopBot CNC routers, a medium and a large one. "We've been working with TechShops and other kinds of makerspaces, trying to develop strategies for supporting customers in environments like that, because it's quite a bit different than a small business or a manufacturing operation owning a tool," says Ted Hall, ShopBot founder and CEO. "You have dozens of people using a tool in a given week, and they're all using it in different ways. Mostly, they're relatively inexperienced, so it's a tough environment for a technology tool to be robust and reliable in."

That's where Dream Consultants come in. Along with many other responsibilities, these TechShop employees help keep up the machines. They also police the equipment, offer general help, and act as a friend and liaison to the community.

"You're kind of a central hub for not only knowledge but social capital. You know what everyone's working on, pretty much, within the shop at all times," says Mel Olivares, who trains DCs, as he calls them, across the system. "You're part of the glue that makes the atmosphere happen. It's much more than just a manufacturing consultant."

That community is a crucial part of the protocol, too, both Hatch and Newton note. They have settled on a minimum goal of approximately 500 paying members per TechShop, not just because that makes them profitable, but also because they believe that's where the community hits critical mass. "There's magic that happens around the community aspect once you hit 500 members," says Hatch. "There's a flip in their mindset; they come in because they want to, they want to experience the community, they want to see their friends, they want to hang out a little bit longer."

The community factors heavily into one of their favorite success stories: Type A Machines. Type A built 3D printers at the San Francisco location. As the company grew — it has sold more than $1 million worth of printers so far — it moved to a manufacturing facility in nearby San Leandro. Though many run businesses out of TechShop, it really isn't suitable for large-scale production runs, largely because someone may be using the machine you need when you have to get a shipment out. But Type A kept its headquarters in a rented office on the company's top floor and a membership for R&D and prototyping. "This TechShop location has an unbeatable team and we couldn't have done it the way we did without

6

7

8. Every tool has its place.

9. The Jet variable speed, 3-horsepower vertical milling machine, equipped with a digital display, allows TechShop members to adjust the tool without using the mechanical dials. "This would be a dream machine to have in your own home," says Newton.

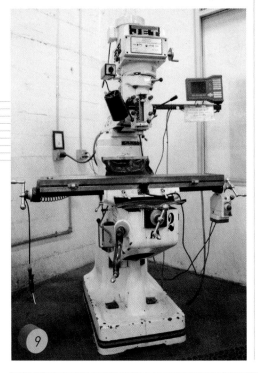

them," says Miloh Alexander, co-founder and hardware engineer for Type A.

"We use the SF TechShop tools like the mill, laser cutters, and other tools to build parts for our plywood machines and our 2014 folded metal machines, which we ship fully assembled and offer service and support for," adds Alexander. "From the start we've needed TechShop tools to be able to closely manage the process of building strange machines that ... make a variety of strange things."

Building strange machines, in a way, is what led Newton to found TechShop. He entered a BattleBots competition and built a 220-pound fighting robot. He had no lathe or mill to build the gearboxes or axles, so he enrolled in a shop class at the College of San Mateo, just to use their tools, and it became a model. "I realized right there that ... it's so hard to get access to a good complement of equipment, that people would actually pay for access," he says.

Despite the demand, exhibited years ago by Newton and other makers enrolling or even teaching classes just to get access to shops, it remains a tenuous business model. "As more makerspaces come online with community at their core, I think a new sustainable business model will emerge," says Taylor.

TechShop attacks the problem via partnerships at its new locations. Ford in Detroit and Lowe's in Austin, Texas, have given employees memberships. In Arlington, TechShop also teamed with DARPA. In the next shops planned in Dublin and Munich, the company is partnering with Dublin City University and BMW, respectively. A planned Los Angeles shop is in partnership with a maker community called The Reef, and one in St. Louis is still seeking investors.

Hatch tossed out 2020 as a possible date for his 60- to 100-store goal, but added that he has no idea if that's realistic. Beyond that, he sees the company getting into distributed manufacturing, design, and prototyping services.

"We really see TechShop eventually looking and operating similar to how Kinko's operates today, where people can choose whether or not to come in and make something themselves, or they can ship us the file and we can make it for them," says Hatch, who was formerly director of computer services at Kinko's. "As manufacturing continues down the automation path, continues down the digitization path, and we continue to open up more locations, working on more sophisticated tools, we will be able to position ourselves as basically the largest distributed manufacturing company in the world." ◗

MASTERING TECHSHOP IN 12 EASY STEPS

»1. Get set up with your photo-equipped RFID badge. You'll need it to get in the door and to get certified on TechShop equipment.

»2. Meet the staff and Dream Consultants; they're there to help you and they'll get you engaged in the community.

»3. Take a safety class for a machine you know you'll need.

»4. Go shopping at the TechShop retail store. They have many of the materials you need in small quantities, perfect for a single project.

»5. Build a project you've been planning — or dreaming of — for a long time. Hire a Dream Consultant if you don't know how.

»6. Take a 3D design class; it'll introduce you to many tools, from 3D printers to laser cutters to CNC mills and routers.

»7. Create something and give it away.

»8. Buy an expert a beer and pick her brain.

»9. Pick a class that looks interesting, something you've never tried before. That machine will become a tool in your belt — you'll see its potential and come up with ideas for how to use it.

»10. Reverse engineer something.

»11. Go back and build something again, but better. That's how you become an expert.

»12. Create something and sell it. There have never been more ways to sell your projects, from Etsy to Kickstarter to Tindie.

BAND SAW · DRILL PRESS · MILL · LASER CUTTER · WELDER · CNC ROUTER · 3D PRINTER · TABLE SAW

HOW TO MAKE A MAKERSPACE

Written by Molly Rubenstein

SIX THINGS YOU DON'T REALIZE
YOU SHOULD KNOW BEFORE GETTING STARTED

**MOLLY
RUBENSTEIN**

An educator, performer, and community organizer by trade, she is a member of the team responsible for growing the Artisan's Asylum (artisansasylum. com) from a small maker clubhouse to a giant community center and business incubator in Somerville, Massachusetts. In her limited free time, she tries to help prepare makerspace founders around the world for success.

SO YOU'RE GOING TO RALLY YOUR LOCAL MAK- ERS INTO A COLLABORATIVE, COMMUNITY-BASED WORKPLACE. You'll need a location, which can range from a mobile pop-up stored in your van to an 80,000-square-foot warehouse. You'll need tools, which can be borrowed from members, donated by sponsors, or purchased. You'll need a business plan.

After that, it's all in the details. Here are six tips that you may not be thinking about yet but should be.

ASK FOR HELP
Your success will depend on finding a strong team to help you. Plus, there's nothing that unites a commu- nity like a good volunteer build-out. Call everyone in to clean the space, paint the walls, move things around, and build some furniture. It is a makerspace, after all — have the first group project be the space itself.

BUILD WHAT PEOPLE WANT
You can design a multimillion-dollar, state-of-the-art facility, only to discover that everyone just wants a place where they can draw on the walls. Design the space for the community you have.

TO DIY OR NOT TO DIY
There's always some member or volunteer who says we should do it ourselves. For building benches for the

woodshop, that's great. But for legal contracts, ac- counting, and wiring, make sure you find an expert.

IMAGINE THE BEST ...
When planning your infrastructure and setting a vision with your community, imagine what you would do with a million dollars. Would you get the biggest space? Move to a prime location? Get the shiniest tools? Or offer all your services for free?

... BUDGET FOR THE WORST
Expect delays of all kinds. You might have to pay rent and utilities for months before you generate revenue. However long you think it will take to open, triple that.

YOU ARE NOT ALONE!
Others are solving these same problems all over the world. Visit their spaces, talk to the people who run them, check out Maker Media's handbook, *The Maker- space Workbench*. There might even be a local library, university, or economic development office that's think- ing about doing the same thing.

Don't worry; what you're doing is hard but not impos- sible. Some of these things we did right at Artisan's Asylum the first time, and some of them we had to learn the hard way. Good luck! ⊘

Photo: Artisan's Asylum. Illustration: James Burke

SKILL BUILDER+

EASY TO ADVANCED

CUSTOM SOUND

by Charles Platt and Fredrik Jansson

Learn to shape sound waves with timer chips to create your own digital sampling system emulator.

**Time Required:
2-7 Hours
Cost:
$10-$30**

CHARLES PLATT
is the author of *Make: Electronics*, an introductory guide for all ages. He has completed a sequel, *Make: More Electronics*, and is also the author of Volume One of the *Encyclopedia of Electronic Components*. Volumes Two and Three are in preparation. makershed.com/platt

FREDRIK JANSSON
is a physicist from Finland, currently living in Amsterdam, where he simulates sea animals. He enjoys cheese, Belgian beer, and tinkering with electronics. Occasionally he blogs about projects together with his wife.

A Installation of a 3" speaker in a plastic project box. Nuts have nylon inserts to guard against loosening from vibration. The rear panel of the box must be attached to achieve acceptable sound.

B Holes must be large enough to transmit sound while providing protection for the speaker cone. Start with a 1/16" drill bit and work up in small steps to the final size, to avoid fracturing the plastic.

Sound Synthesis Basics

Anyone familiar with a 555 timer knows that it can create audible frequencies. What you may not have considered is that a timer can manipulate waveforms to create different *kinds* of sounds. You can actually custom-build your own audio waveform, one digital slice at a time.

The Output Device

Because accidents may happen, you may not want to use a high-quality loudspeaker in this experiment. Still, you do need one that can reproduce a reasonable range of frequencies. A 3" (75mm) speaker costing around $5 should be adequate, provided it's mounted in a resonant enclosure such as a project box. See **A** and **B**.

Versatile Timing

I chose a 14538B chip for my first venture into sound synthesis, because it's loaded with options that were missing from the old 555 chip. It contains two monostable timers, each with two trigger pins and two output pins. One trigger is sensitive to a rising edge, while the other responds to a falling edge. One output is active-high, while the other is active-low. Pinouts are shown in **C**.

The pulse duration from each timer is set with one resistor and one capacitor. If *R* is resistance

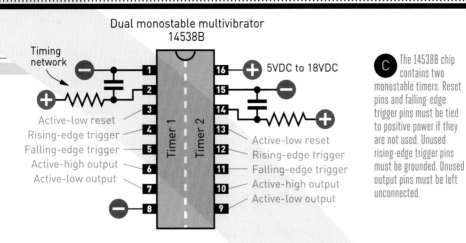

Dual monostable multivibrator
14538B

Timing network

Active-low reset
Rising-edge trigger
Falling-edge trigger
Active-high output
Active-low output

5VDC to 18VDC

Active-low reset
Rising-edge trigger
Falling-edge trigger
Active-high output
Active-low output

C The 14538B chip contains two monostable timers. Reset pins and falling-edge trigger pins must be tied to positive power if they are not used. Unused rising-edge trigger pins must be grounded. Unused output pins must be left unconnected.

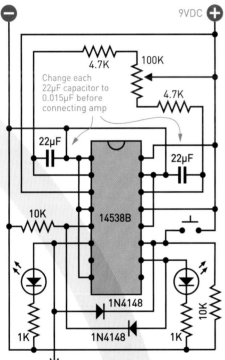

9VDC

4.7K   100K

Change each 22µF capacitor to 0.015µF before connecting amp

4.7K

22µF   22µF

10K   14538B

1N4148

1K   1N4148   1K   10K

To LM386 amplifier

D This test circuit will generate pulse pairs summing to approximately 2 seconds.

E Output pulses from one timer in the 14538B chip are separated by pauses created by the other timer. The trimmer potentiometer creates different waveforms that have the same frequency.

in kilohms and *C* is capacitance in microfarads, you can determine the pulse time, in seconds, using this formula:

$$T = (R \times C) / 1,000$$

For example, a 22µF capacitor with a 100K resistor will create a pulse lasting 2.2 seconds.

Each timer only runs in monostable mode, but they can trigger each other to create a pulse stream. A circuit to achieve this is shown in **D**. My plan is for Timer 1 to create a pulse, after which Timer 2 will create a delay before the next pulse, and the combination will constitute a single cycle in a sound wave. To make the changes in sound quality easier to hear, the frequency must remain constant, which is achieved by controlling the two timers with two sides of a potentiometer. When one timer speeds up, the other slows down by an equal amount, and the output should look like the graphs in **E**.

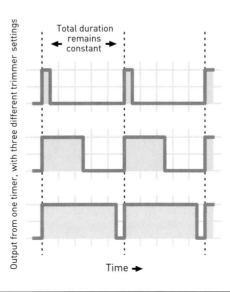

Output from one timer, with three different trimmer settings

Total duration remains constant

Time →

Materials

» **Hookup wire**
» **Solder**
» **Loudspeaker, 8Ω, 3" approximate diameter**
» **Project box: 6"×4"×2"** big enough for the loudspeaker, such as RadioShack 270-1806
» **Battery, 9V, and terminal connector with stripped wire ends**

NOTE: THERE ARE 3 MINI PROJECTS CONTAINED IN THIS SKILL BUILDER. SOME PROJECT COMPONENTS MUST BE REUSED IN SUBSEQUENT PROJECTS.

FOR PROJECT 1:

» **Resistors: 1kΩ (2), 4.7kΩ (2), 6.8kΩ (1), 10kΩ (3)**
» **Trimmer potentiometers: 100Ω, 100kΩ, 250kΩ, 500kΩ (1 of each)**
» **Capacitors: 22µF (2), 0.015µF (2), 330µF (1)**
» **Small signal diodes, 1N4148 (2)**
» **LEDs, generic, 20mA forward current (2)**
» **Dual monostable timer chip, 14538B** any manufacturer*
» **Amplifier chip, LM386** any version

ADDITIONAL FOR PROJECT 2:

» **Trimmer potentiometers: 1kΩ (3), 20kΩ or 25kΩ (3)**
» **Capacitors: 0.01µF (4), 0.068µF (4), 1µF (4), 1.5µF (1), 2.2µF (1)**
» **Timer chips, NE555P or similar (4)**

ADDITIONAL FOR PROJECT 3:

» **Trimmer potentiometer, 20kΩ or 25kΩ (1)**
» **Capacitors: 0.022µF (2), 0.033µF (3), 0.1µF (3), 10µF (1)**
» **Counter chip, 4520B** any manufacturer*
» **Multiplexer chip, 4067B** any manufacturer*

NOTE: CHIPS MUST BE DIP OR PDIP FORMAT, NOT SURFACE-MOUNT.

Tools

» **Soldering iron**
» **Multimeter** preferably able to measure capacitance
» **Solderless breadboard**
» **Drill and bits**

* Part number may be preceded and followed by letters

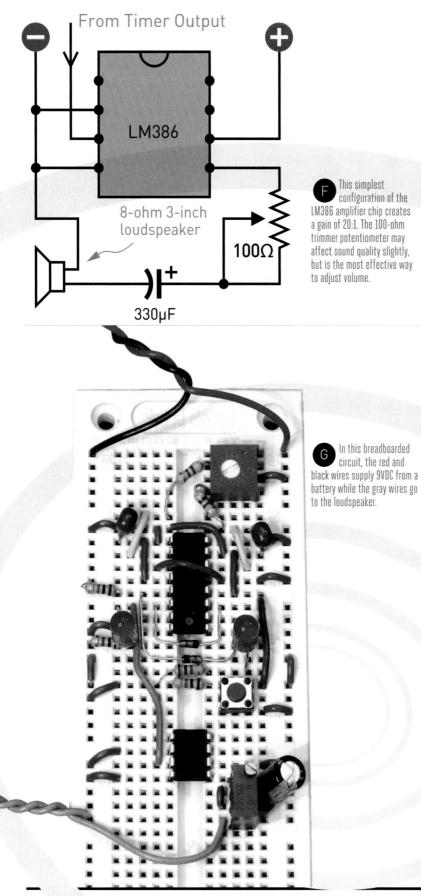

From Timer Output

LM386

8-ohm 3-inch
loudspeaker

100Ω

330µF

F This simplest configuration of the LM386 amplifier chip creates a gain of 20:1. The 100-ohm trimmer potentiometer may affect sound quality slightly, but is the most effective way to adjust volume.

G In this breadboarded circuit, the red and black wires supply 9VDC from a battery while the gray wires go to the loudspeaker.

Powering Up

The 14538B operates with a supply of 5V to 18V, and it can be powered with a 9V battery. No voltage regulation is required. Output current is restricted to 10mA, so a 1K resistor must be used with each LED.

When you apply power, nothing happens — because the two timers are waiting for each other. Press and release the tactile switch to create the falling edge required at Pin 11 to trigger Timer 2. When its high output ends, Timer 2 triggers Timer 1 on Pin 5. This to-and-fro process continues indefinitely, as the timers play tag with each other.

Small signal diodes prevent each timer from trying to force a positive voltage into the output of the other. The LEDs show what's going on. Turn the trimmer to and fro, and watch how they swap the long and short cycles.

Mini Project 1: EASY
The Sound of Sound

If the concept is now clear, let's crank the frequency to an audible value. I chose 600 pulses per second — that is, 600Hz. Remove the two 22µF capacitors and substitute two 0.015µF capacitors. If your meter will measure capacitance, select capacitors whose actual values are as close to each other as possible. This will ensure that the output frequency remains constant when you turn the trimmer.

The 14538B isn't powerful enough to drive a speaker, so you will need an amplifier. An LM386 chip will do. Wire it as shown in **F**. A photograph of the complete breadboarded circuit appears in **G**.

Connect the power, press the tactile switch, and listen while you turn the trimmer. When the high pulse and the low pulse are about equal, the sound is mellow, but at opposite ends of the scale it becomes edgier. This is because the shape of the sound wave determines how many *harmonics* will be audible — the higher frequencies that are a multiple of the one that's dominant.

Remove the 100K trimmer and substitute a 250K trimmer. This creates a richer range of sounds, because the lower frequency allows more room for harmonics. If you mounted your speaker in a resonant box as I suggested, a 500K trimmer should sound best of all. To learn more about harmonics, try the online tutorial at thedawstudio.com/Tips/Soundwaves.html.

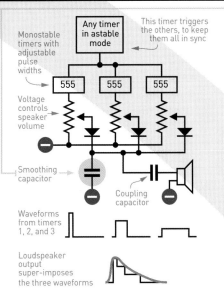

Monostable timers with adjustable pulse widths

Any timer in astable mode

This timer triggers the others, to keep them all in sync

Voltage controls speaker volume

Smoothing capacitor

Coupling capacitor

Waveforms from timers 1, 2, and 3

Loudspeaker output super-imposes the three waveforms

H Pulses of differing voltage and duration may be superimposed to create a stairstepped audio waveform. Three bipolar 555 timers run in monostable mode, synchronized by a fourth astable timer.

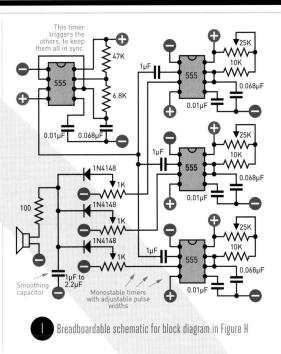

This timer triggers the others, to keep them all in sync.

Smoothing capacitor

Monostable timers with adjustable pulse widths

I Breadboardable schematic for block diagram in Figure H

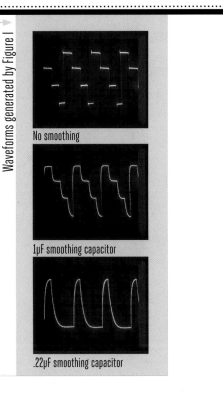

Waveforms generated by Figure I

No smoothing

1µF smoothing capacitor

.22µF smoothing capacitor

Mini Project 2: `MODERATE`
Advanced Wave Building

You can go much further into shaping a sound wave. **H** shows a concept for a circuit using four 555 timers of the old bipolar type (also known as the TTL type) which can drive a loudspeaker directly. The first timer creates a stream of pulses, triggering the other three timers simultaneously. Each of them is running in one-shot mode for durations that are separately adjustable, and each output goes through a trimmer that is tapped to provide a variable voltage for the loudspeaker. The unequal pulse lengths combine to create different sized horizontal slices of a sound wave. See **I** for the breadboard schematic.

Mini Project 3: `ADVANCED`
Digital Sampling System Emulator

If you want to go still further, you can build an ultrasimple, bargain-basement circuit that emulates the sampling system used in all digital recordings. **J** shows the concept. A multiplexer samples each potentiometer very rapidly and sends its voltage through an amplifier to the speaker. **K** is the breadboard schematic for this.

We've been listening to digitally replicated sounds ever since Sony and Philips developed the first audio CDs some 35 years ago. Because the frequencies are actually quite slow by digital standards, all you need is a little imagination to process them with that most basic and familiar component, the timer chip. ✪

Timer in astable mode

Voltage dividers

Divide-by-8 counter

Multiplexer

Multiplexer connects each voltage divider with amplifier in ABCDCBA sequence followed by a zero-voltage pause

Amplifier

A B C D C B A   A B C D C B A

J In this concept, a multiplexer rapidly selects voltages adjusted by potentiometers to build a symmetrical audio waveform.

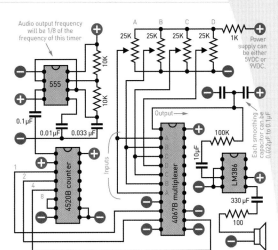

Audio output frequency will be 1/8 of the frequency of this timer

Power supply can be either 5VDC or 9VDC.

Output

Each smoothing capacitor can be 0.022µF to 0.1 µF

4520B counter

4067B multiplexer

LM386

K Breadboardable schematic for block diagram in Figure J.

EASY

THE SKINNY ON

End Mills

Written by Tyler Worman ■ Illustrated by Rob Nance
Photos by Anna Kaziunas France

Don't be intimidated by CNC routing. Take the first step into machining by gaining a solid understanding of subtractive tooling basics.

INTERESTED IN CNC ROUTING BUT CLUELESS ABOUT TOOLING? Can't tell an end mill from a drill bit? Here's an overview of end mill anatomy, some basic cutter types, and tips on how to choose the correct tooling for basic wood or plastic jobs.

Drill Bits vs. End Mills

CNC machining is a subtractive process that uses rotational cutting tools called "end mills" to remove material. An end mill, while similar in appearance to a drill bit, is far more versatile.

However, in practice the terms "bit" and "end mill" are often used interchangeably. Here's the key difference. Drill bits are designed to plunge directly into material, cutting axially and creating cylindrical holes. **A** End mills are typically used for horizontal carving and cut laterally. **B**

Additionally, most mills are "center-cutting," meaning they are able to cut both axially and laterally. This is due to cutting flutes that extend to — and protrude from — the end face and enable plunge cutting.

To minimize tool breakage and stress on the material being cut, most CNC software will "ramp" the end mill slowly into lateral cuts. **C**

The project type, material being cut, and desired surface finish determines the tool geometry. Key tooling features include the diameter, shank,

flutes, teeth, tip shape, center cutting capability, helix angle, helix direction, length of cut, and overall tool length. **D**

Tip Shapes and Applications

Each tip shape is designed for a particular purpose. Drill bits have a pointed center tip **E**, while common end mill tip geometries include: fish tail, ballnose, straight, surface planing and v-bits. **F**

Fish tail cutters will produce a flat surface, while ballnose mills produce a rounded pass and are ideal for 3D contour work. V-bits produce a "V" shaped pass and are used for engraving, particularly for making signs. **G**

Flutes and Chipload

Flutes are the helical grooves that wrap around the sides of the end mill. Each flute has a single tooth with a sharp cutting edge (although there can be more than one) that runs along the edge of the flute.

As the tooth cuts into the wood, each flute whisks away a small section or "chip." The fewer the flutes, the more material that is ejected with each tool rotation. **H**

Chipload is the thickness of a machined chip as cut by a specific tool type. More flutes create a smoother surface finish, while fewer flutes remove material fastest, but make rougher cuts.

See our full tutorial (makezine.com/endmills)

TYLER WORMAN
I'm a maker and software developer living in Ann Arbor, Michigan. I love playing with new microcontrollers and experimenting with rapid prototyping tools.

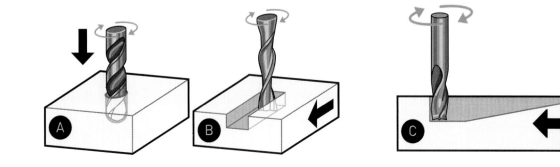

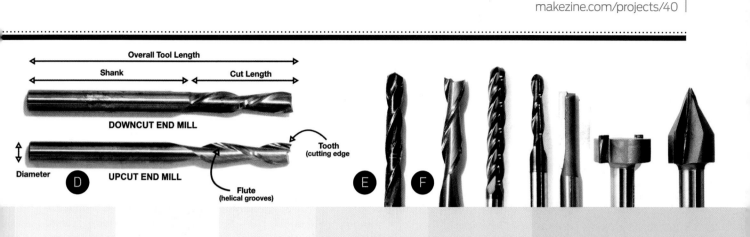

Overall Tool Length
Shank
Cut Length
DOWNCUT END MILL
Diameter
D **UPCUT END MILL**
Tooth (cutting edge
Flute (helical grooves)

E **F**

for more detail, but proper chipload is important because chips dissipate heat. Hot cutters can lead to suboptimal results, including burned wood, a poor edge finish and dull tooling.

If you're machining a material like HDPE plastic, you want to use an "0" or single flute bit to clear the chips away as quickly as possible or heat will build up and melt the plastic, which can "reweld" to the tool.

Helical Direction, Chip Ejection and Surfaces Produced

A CNC router spins a cutter clockwise. The helical direction of the flutes as they wrap around the tool determine if chips are ejected towards the top or bottom of the workpiece.

True to their name, upcut mills eject chips towards the top of the workpiece, producing a cleanly cut bottom surface. The downside is possible surface splintering or "tearout" on the top surface as the chips are ejected upwards. **I**

Downcut tools do the opposite, producing a smooth upper surface. They are ideal for pieces that have been previously engraved or v-carved and cannot be flipped to hide tearout. In addition, as downcut mills pack the chips into the cut path, they can be used instead of tabs to hold down a workpiece and keep it from moving.

Which Cutters to Buy First?

If you are looking to purchase a great wood and plastic starter set, consider picking up a few of the following carbide tool types in ¼" and ⅛" diameters:

- 2 flute upcut and downcut end mills (great for hardwood and plywood)
- 2 or 4 flute ballnose mill (great for 3D contours)
- Single or "0" flute mill (great for plastics like HDPE and acrylic)
- 60° or 90° v-bit (great for cutting hardwood signs)

The quality of your work can be significantly improved by selecting the right tooling for your project and materials — plus you'll spend less time on hand-finishing. ✸

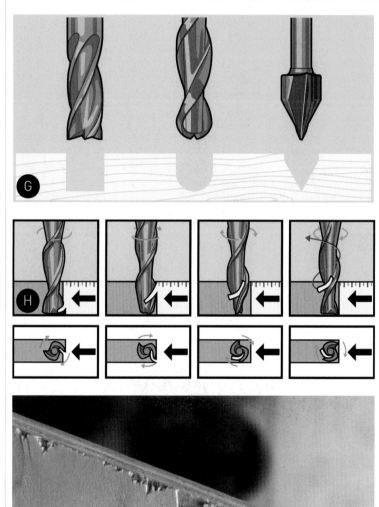

G

H

I

Time Required:
2-3 Hours,
Cost:
$40-$150

R/C Omniwheel Robot

Build an easy holonomic "Kiwi drive" robot platform that moves instantly in any direction.

Written and Photographed by Dirk Swart

Gunther Kirsch

DIRK SWART
is a co-founder of Wicked Device LLC, a maker of fun electronics kits.

A ROBOT THAT CAN MOVE IN ANY DIRECTION IMMEDIATELY is useful for getting around tight spaces and for behaviors like chasing (or fleeing). No matter how fast an R/C car is, there's no way it can catch something that can instantly go any direction, even sideways. Regular car-style robots can't drive sideways, but omniwheel robots can!

An *omniwheel* is a wheel whose tread is made up of a bunch of little rollers. They're used commercially for things like transfer tables on production lines, and this means they're cheap and reliable. In this proj-

ect you'll use them to build a *Kiwi drive* robot platform — a three-omniwheel vehicle that can travel in any direction. It's mesmerizing to watch, and it can even rotate while traveling, so it's great for turret-type applications too.

If a robot can drive in any direction immediately, it is called *holonomic* — it has two degrees of freedom on the floor. Cars, where all the wheels line up, can't move at right angles to their wheels, so they're not holonomic.

Omniwheels can move at 90 degrees to their axis, so you can mount them facing different directions on

2a

2b

Materials

» **Arduino Uno microcontroller board** Maker Shed item #MKSP99, makershed.com
» *Make:* **Motor Shield for Arduino** Maker Shed #MSMOT01

NEW! CO-DEVELOPED WITH WICKED DEVICE, OUR AWESOME NEW MOTOR SHIELD CAN RUN 4 DC MOTORS (1.2A–3A MAX), OR 2 STEPPERS AND 6 SERVOS. IT HAS CURRENT SENSING SO YOU CAN USE MOTORS AS SENSORS, AND IT ACCEPTS R/C INPUTS FROM STANDARD RADIO CONTROL GEAR! NO SOLDERING REQUIRED. MAKER SHED #MSMOT01

» **Omniwheels, 2" diameter (3)** aka poly wheels. I used Transwheels 2000 Series rubber-coated ("cat-trak") wheels, part #2051 at kornylak.com (plain nylon wheels are too slippery). You can order small quantities from Wicked Device, part #TRANSWHEEL1.
» **Battery holder, 4×AA or 6×AA**
» **R/C transmitter module** OrangeRX DMS2/DSMX is a good choice. This fits inside a typical R/C transmitter like the Turnigy TGY-9X.
» **R/C receiver** The OrangeRx R615 Spektrum/JR DSM2 is about $6 and works well.
» **Gearmotors, 5V DC (3)** Wicked Device #MOTO1, wickeddevice.com. If you want more powerful 12V motors, then Jameco #159418 is a good choice.
» **R/C servo cable** or Wicked Device part #FLICKCABLE
» **Mounting platform and hardware** Available as a kit including the wheels, Wicked Device #OMNI1, or you can cut your own platform (6" circular or triangular) and acrylic disks (1/8" or 0.118") to mount to motors to the omniwheels.
» **Wire, 22AWG solid copper, insulated** in red and black
For optional enclosure:
» **Acrylic sheet, 1/8" nominal thickness (0.118"), about 12"×24"**
» **Machine screws, M3×10mm, with nuts (4)**

your vehicle and use a bit of math to still go in a straight line. (That's where a microcontroller comes in handy.) Like most things in engineering, there are some tradeoffs, which is why we don't all drive omniwheel cars. They're slower, sensitive to dust, can take less load — only a few pounds for the wheels we're using — and they're less efficient. But in tight spaces they're the right choice, and a lot of fun!

Our omniwheel robot is a beginner-friendly build that uses an Arduino microcontroller, the new *Make:* Motor Shield, and standard R/C gear — all of it plug-and-play.

> **NOTE:** WITH DC MOTORS, IT DOESN'T MATTER WHICH SIDE IS POSITIVE (+) AND WHICH IS NEGATIVE (–). BUT MAKE SURE ALL 3 MOTORS ARE WIRED THE SAME WAY OR YOUR ROBOT WILL END UP DRIVING IN CIRCLES, BECAUSE ONE MOTOR WILL BE GOING BACKWARD.

1. Solder wires to the motors
Then test each motor by connecting it to the battery pack — just twist the wires together — to make sure the wheels turn smoothly. The motor terminal tabs are fragile, so be careful with the wires until they're glued down.

2. Attach the wheels
Cut disks from 1/8" (0.118") acrylic following the provided template *wheel1.svg*, and super-glue them together as shown. Then glue the larger disks to the omniwheels, and the smaller disks directly to the motors as shown (**Figures 2a** and **2b**).

3. Mount the motors
Use double-stick tape to mount the motors to the platform, following the template *base1. svg* to make sure the motor shafts are lined up correctly, 120° apart. Put a dab of hot glue on each pair of wires to hold them down (**Figure 3**).

4. Route the motor wires
Drill 3 holes to pass the motor wires through the platform. The platform will want to run

3

4

up the drill bit, so hold it down firmly.
Route the wires through the holes. Test each motor with the battery pack again (**Figure 4**).

5. Add the electronics
Turn the platform over so the motors are on the bottom. On top, stack the battery pack, an insulating sheet of paper or plastic, the Arduino, and the *Make:* Motor Shield (in that order). I used little rubber feet on the Arduino, but double-stick tape will work as well.

Make sure the motor shield switch is in the Off position, then connect the battery pack to + and –, and the motors to pins M1, M2, and M3 on the shield (**Figure 5**).

Tools

» **Soldering iron and solder**
» **Small (jeweler's) Phillips screwdriver**
» **Super glue or epoxy**
» **Double-stick tape** Scotch Extreme Mounting Tape is ideal.
» **Hot glue gun**
» **Computer with Arduino IDE** software free download from arduino.cc
» **Project code** Get the Arduino sketch *OmniWheelControl.ino* at github.com/WickedDevice/OmniWheelControl
» **Laser cutter (optional)**

5

6

8a

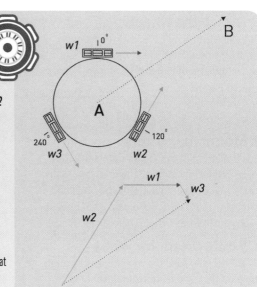

8b

6. Connect the receiver

Follow the manufacturer's instructions to pair your R/C receiver with your transmitter.

Run an R/C servo cable from your receiver to the 2 RC_IN ports on the motor shield. Black (ground) is toward the middle of the shield. I used the rudder (RUDD) and aileron (AILE) connections of my R/C receiver, which map to the left-hand transmitter joystick (**Figure 6**).

7. Program the Arduino

Connect your Arduino to your computer with a USB cable. Download the sketch *OmniWheelControl.ino* from makezine.com/projects/kiwi, open it in the Arduino IDE, and click the arrow button to upload it to your board.

You'll also need the Motor Shield library; download it at github.com/WickedDevice/

> **TIP:**
> WHEN REMOVING A JUMP-ER, DON'T TRY TO STORE IT AWAY FROM THE BOARD — IT'S TINY AND EASY TO LOSE. INSTEAD, DISCONNECT IT FROM ONE PIN ONLY, AND LET IT HANG. THIS BREAKS THE CONNECTION, BUT KEEPS THE JUMPER HANDY IF YOU WANT TO RESET IT.

WickedMotorShield then go to the Arduino IDE and install it by selecting Sketch → Import Library.

8. Add a cover (optional)

You can make one out of pretty much anything you like the looks of. At makezine.com/projects/kiwi you'll find files for laser-cutting a basic box from 1/8" (0.118") acrylic, sized to contain a 6×AA battery pack, the Arduino, the motor shield, and the R/C receiver (**Figures 8a** and **8b**).

9. Take it for a test drive

The motor shield has 2 important jumpers to keep in mind. BEC provides power to the radio receiver, so you don't need an additional power source. EXT provides power to the Arduino using the motor power source, in this case the battery pack.

KIWI DRIVE: CRACK THE CODE:

Your robot has 3 wheels, all pointing in different directions — how on Earth is it going to drive in a straight line? It requires some sophisticated math, so you can't drive this vehicle without a computer. The Arduino code turns the radio control signals into motor power signals for each motor. But how?

1. A radio control signal is a little bit like a pulse-width modulation signal (PWM), but not quite. The R/C transmitter creates signal pulses, and the Arduino reads these in on pins Dig4 (R/C input 1, on the right) and Dig8 (R/C input 2, on the left, near the other jumpers).

2. The Arduino converts the R/C signals to PWM motor drive signals, using the PulseIn command.

3. Next, the Arduino sketch applies vector math formulas to break the motor signal's single vector (A–B) into 3 vectors, one for each wheel (w1, w2, and w3). The Arduino works all this out for you on the fly, sends the new drive signals to each motor, and the vehicle drives! To learn more about Kiwi drive math, visit the project page at makezine.com/projects/kiwi.

Make sure both these jumpers are connected and that there are fresh batteries in the holder.

The switch on the motor shield powers up the motors — this is so you can experiment with a robot on your desk without having it drive off suddenly. Turn it on now. Turn on your transmitter and try moving the sticks. If everything's working, you should now have a working R/C holonomic robot!

NOTE: WHEN NOT OPERATING THE ROBOT, DISCONNECT THE POWER JUMPERS AND TURN OFF THE MOTOR POWER SWITCH TO SAVE BATTERIES. (I GOT 6 HOURS OF NEAR-CONTINUOUS USE OUT OF 4 DURACELLS AT MAKER FAIRE, SO IT'S PRETTY EFFICIENT.)

Going Further

Once you've driven your robot around a bit, you'll probably notice that it can be hard to tell front from back. An easy fix is to attach an arrow, a face, or some other prominent decoration on one side.

For more of a challenge, add a Nerf gun to the vehicle. Since it can "strafe" sideways without turning, it can slide out from cover, shoot, and then slide quickly back. Use a servo-operated mechanism to pull the trigger.

Try adding a camera setup for spying, FPV driving, or even a telepresence robot. Or make a pair of kiwi bots to play laser tag or robot soccer.

Finally, let's talk about a scaled-up Kiwi drive. The math and the code should work with vehicles of any size, and bigger omniwheels (like the Kornylak RW27) can easily support a person on a set of three. R/C mobile barstool, anyone? ❂

Get templates and code, share your omni bot, and learn more about holonomic drive at makezine.com/projects/kiwi
Share it: *#makeprojects*

Killer Kiwis

What else can you do with a *Make:* Motor Shield and a Kiwi drive robot? Try these ideas — and share yours at makezine.com/projects/kiwi.

Laser Battle Bots
Use one R/C stick to drive and the other to rotate, just like your favorite first-person-shooter video games. On each bot, add a laser pointer and a light sensor, protected inside a short piece of pipe so that only direct hits are detected!

"Dr. Evil" Frickin Rotating Chair
Scale up to big omniwheels, 12V motors, and an oversized R/C joystick to build a go-anywhere villain's throne that also spins on command (or, like the original, randomly). The math and the code should work with vehicles of any size, and bigger omniwheels (like the Kornylak RW27) can handle 200lb loads apiece.

Ball Balancing Robot
Use brushless DC motors and add an IMU to build an astonishing bot that drives any direction while balancing on top of a ball. You'll have one remaining DC motor connection and 6 servo connections to build functionality on top. Serve beverages like Artoo on Jabba's sail barge?

Cat Tormentor
Chase kitty with your basic Kiwi bot, and mount a laser pointer on a two-servo pan-tilt rig to give kitty something to chase too.

Make a Modern
MOBILE

Swivels and a weight give
flexibility and stability to this
contemporary design.
Written and photographed by Marco Mahler

MARCO MAHLER
is a kinetic sculptor
specializing in
mobiles. In his 14
years of making them,
he has designed and
made a wide variety
of retail mobiles, large
custom mobiles, and
3D-printed mobiles.
He currently lives in
Richmond, Virginia.

ALEXANDER CALDER, INVENTOR OF MODERN MOBILES, CONSTRUCTED HIS CLASSIC MODELS FROM WIRE AND SHEET METAL. This mobile is based on Calder's mid-century modern mobiles, yet I'd like to think it has a contemporary design element to it.

Conventional mobiles are mostly made with hook-into-loop connections, which restrict movement to some extent. My mobile uses swivels, which allow the parts to rotate full circle, independent from each other.

It also has a weight attached, which gives the balance points more flexibility and makes the mobile a little easier to build. The weight also gives the mobile more stability, making it better equipped to hang in a windy spot or outdoors.

Finished, it will measure approximately 30" (75cm) in both height and diameter, which fits an average-sized room nicely.

Mobiles are constructed from the bottom up, meaning you start with the lowest part because the balance of the higher parts depends on the weight of the lower ones. A mobile with a weight attached like this one gives you quite a bit of flexibility on the balance points. You can increase or decrease the angle of the arms going out from the loop to point more upward or downward.

1. Create the shapes
Download and print the template PDF at makezine.com/calder-mobile, and trim out the shapes (**Figure 1a**).

Trace the shapes onto the sheet metal with a dry- or wet-erase pen, making sure to mark the drill holes. Cut them out with tinsnips (**Figure 1b**).

Using the ⁵⁄₆₄" bit, drill the 2 holes traced into each shape (**Figure 1c**).

2. Flatten and smooth
Hammer the edges of the shapes flat, then sand off any jagged edges either by hand or using a powered sanding tool.

TIP: A CHEAP ALTERNATIVE IS TO GET A SANDING DRILL BIT. WITH ONE HAND YOU CAN HOLD THE DRILL FLAT ON A TABLETOP WHILE YOU MOVE THE SHEET METAL SHAPE ALONG THE ROTATING SANDING BIT.

3. Prepare the ceiling hook
Clip off a 2" length of wire with the needlenose pliers and bend it into a hook — nothing fancy, a simple S-shape will do (**Figure 3**).

Find or install a hook, screw, or nail in the ceiling, tie fishing line to it, and attach the wire hook to the line at an easy-to-reach height.

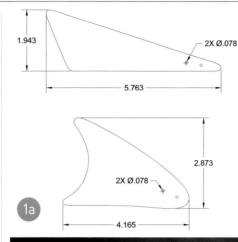

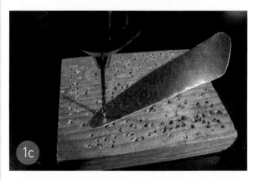

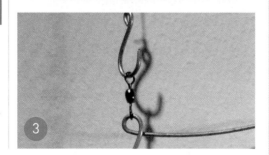

Time Required:
½–1 Day
Cost:
$40–$90

Materials
» **Steel wire, 16 gauge (0.05"),** about 6'–8' total length
» **Sheet metal, 26 gauge (0.022"),** at least 7"x12"
» **Hook, screw, or nail** for hanging
» **Fishing weight, 6oz**
» **Fishing swivels, size 7 (5)**
» **Monofilament fishing line**
» **Paint (optional)**

Tools
» **Needlenose pliers**
» **Tinsnips**
» **Drill and ⁵⁄₆₄" bit**
» **Hammer**
» **Sander, sandpaper, or sanding bit**
» **Dry- or wet-erase pen**
» **Scissors**

NOTE: FOR A STURDIER OR OUTDOOR MOBILE, GO WITH THE THICKER 14-GAUGE WIRE AND USE A 3/32" (2.4MM) DRILL BIT.

NOTE: I PREFER THE LOOK OF SIMPLE 3-PIECE FISHING SWIVELS. YOU CAN FIND THEM IN FISHING SUPPLY STORES AND IN MANY OUTDOOR SPORTS AND DISCOUNT STORES. I LIKE HOW THE MOBILES LOOK WITH A BALL-SHAPED FISHING WEIGHT ATTACHED, BUT YOU CAN REALLY USE ANYTHING THAT WEIGHS ABOUT 6 OUNCES.

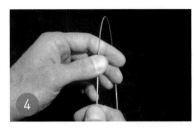

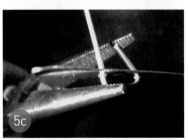

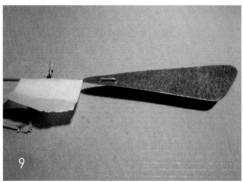

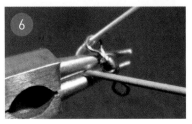

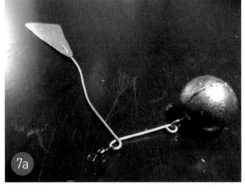

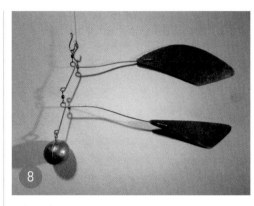

4. Make an arm

Clip off a 12" length of wire and straighten it. I do this by holding one end of the wire with one hand, and with my other hand, extend my thumb and press down while pulling toward the other end. You don't have to get the whole piece perfectly straight, as you'll bend it again, but you'll want one straight end to hook into the sheet metal shape.

Bent wire ends can be hard to straighten out; you can clip them off.

5. Attach a shape

Next, make a hook that'll loop into the 2 holes of the first sheet metal shape (**Figure 5a and 5b**). Hold the straightened wire up to the holes and, using your pliers, give the wire 90° bends at each hole. It can take a little practice to get the size right (**Figure 5c**).

Loop the wire into the sheet metal shape and use pliers to bend both the shorter and the longer end of the wire down flush with the shape, as shown here (**Figure 5d and 5e**). Be careful not to squeeze the wire so much that you end up bending the sheet metal. It doesn't have to be perfectly flat, as long as the wire maintains a decent grip on the shape. Now you have one arm of the mobile with a shape attached to it.

6. Add a swivel

Measure about 4" down the wire from where

the shape ends. Grip the wire with your pliers, thread a swivel onto it, and enclose the swivel in a loop by bending the wire until it reaches a little over 270° of a circle.

From the loop, measure about 2" and clip off the excess wire.

7. Hang the weight

Thread the wire through the eye of the 6oz fishing weight and enclose it in another loop. Now you have the first part of the mobile. You can hang it on the hook you created in Step 3. If needed, adjust the angle of the bend in the wire so that the arm with the shape attached sticks out horizontally (**Figure 7a and 7b**).

8. Repeat and assemble

For the rest of the 5 shapes, simply repeat steps 4–6: Straighten a wire arm, attach it to the sheet metal shape, make a loop with a swivel, and leave about a 2" length of wire. Then bend the second loop through the other eye of the swivel on the previous piece.

The length of the arms, measured from the sheet metal shape to the balance point loop, can be varied. The arms in my mobile, from the lowest to the highest piece, measure 4", 3", 10", 5½", 8½", and 13". All the connecting arms are about 2" long.

You can choose to come up with your own variation of lengths for the arms going out to the shape, however, the other arm going from the loop to the next lower piece needs to be at least 1¾"–2" long. If you leave it shorter than that, you won't be getting enough gravitational pull to hold up the end with the shape.

Once you're done making and attaching all 6 parts, bend the arms a little, this way and that, until you like the way it looks — or, if you choose, until it looks like the finished mobile in the photos.

9. Paint (optional)

I paint my mobiles with either a brush or spray paint, or have them powder coated, although the last option will cost you at least $75 per color, no matter how small the shapes are. That's just the least that most powder coating companies charge for the basic setup per color.

I recommend first roughing up the surface of the shapes with sandpaper to give the paint something to adhere to. If you want to be thorough, apply a primer — my favorite for sheet metal shapes is Insl-X Stix Waterborne Bonding Primer, which costs about $20 a quart.

When applying paint with a brush, I usually have the mobiles hanging on a hook. I recommend applying 2 or 3 thin coats of paint rather than 1 or 2 thick ones. If you apply too much paint in one coat, it will end up collecting on the lower end of the shape, which can look messy.

To spray paint, I lay the mobiles onto cardboard or newspaper, wrap pieces of painter's tape around the wires where they meet the shapes, then prop up the arms with cardboard or other objects in a horizontal position. Spray paint one side of the shapes, wait until it dries, then flip the whole mobile over, prop up the arms again, and paint the other side. Remove the painter's tape when both sides are dry. That's it!

GOING FURTHER

Now that you understand the basics of mobile making, you can experiment with other designs. Take a look at the structures of other mobiles and give them a try. Maybe you'll even invent a completely new type of mobile structure or style. This is still a very young art form, basically less than 100 years old — so there are a lot of new mobile styles and possibilities to be explored! ◑

Share photos of your mobile at makezine.com/calder-mobile. Share it: *#makeprojects*

Fused Filament
Fiddle

3D-print a full-size electric violin, then plug in and play.

Written by David Perry

DAVID PERRY
is owner and engineer at OpenFab PDX, a Portland, Oregon-based consulting firm providing digital design and fabrication services, from CAD design and strategic consulting to 3D printer-themed birthday parties. When he's not designing things to be made by robots, David can be found on a bicycle, thinking about things to print.

THE F-F-FIDDLE (PRONOUNCED EFF-EFF-FIDDLE) IS A FULL-SIZE ELECTRIC VIOLIN, designed in Autodesk's Fusion 360, that can be made on a desktop 3D printer — the fused-filament fabrication (FFF) type. All parts can be printed without support material, and the finished fiddle is fully functional and fun to play!

The current fiddle is the seventh physical prototype and the eighth revision of the design. Each prototype was played and improved for playability. I'm still iterating, and each F-F-Fiddle is a little nicer to play. It sounds good, and I'm ready for others to try it!

Here's how to make your own. For project updates, visit openfabpdx.com/fffiddle.

1. Prepare the 3D-printed parts

Download the STL files from thingiverse.com/thing:219040 and 3D-print them: the bout (print 3 shells at least 10% infill), the neck (print 3 shells at least 10% infill), and the bridge (print at least 2 shells, 5% infill).

If you don't have access to a 3D printer, I also offer F-F-Fiddle parts and kits made to order. You can also send the files to a service that will print the parts and mail them to you; check out makezine.com/where-to-get-digital-fabrication-tool-access.

RECOMMENDED SLICING SETTINGS:

» 0.20mm layer height
» 10% infill
» 3 shells
» 3 solid layers top and bottom

Time Required:
Printing
12-22 Hours,
Assembly
3-6 Hours
Cost:
$250-$300

Materials

- » **3D-printed violin parts: bout, neck, and bridge** see Step 1
- » **Drill rod, ⁵⁄₁₆" dia., 355mm length**
- » **Machine head tuners (4)** Gotoh Stealth model, 2 left-hand, 2 right-hand
- » **Violin strings, 4/4 size**
- » **Piezo transducer pickup** K&K Twin Spot model
- » **Female mono plug for ¼" cable**
- » **Socket head cap screws, #8-32×1½" (2)**
- » **Socket head cap screws, #8-32×1" (2)**
- » **Nuts, #8-32 (4)**
- » **Heat-shrink tubing: large diameter, small diameter**

Tools

- » **Pliers, needlenose**
- » **Files: general purpose, small triangular**
- » **Deburring tool** easier, safer than a knife for cleaning parts
- » **X-Acto knife**
- » **Screwdrivers, small: Phillips, flat-head**
- » **Wire cutter/stripper**
- » **Sandpaper, 220–600 grit**
- » **Soldering station**
- » **Allen wrench, ⁹⁄₆₄"**
- » **Safety glasses**
- » **High-speed rotary tool** for cutting drill rod
- » **Drill with ⁵⁄₁₆" bit**
- » **Calipers and permanent marker**
- » **3D printer (optional)**

2. Cut the truss rod

If you haven't already, cut down the ⁵⁄₁₆" drill rod to 355mm, +/– 2mm. I use a Dremel with a fiber cutoff tool.

Clean off rod ends so that they aren't too sharp to the touch. Keep some edge, though, to allow the rod to cut through any excess plastic. Lightly sand any burrs.

CAUTION: WEAR SAFETY GLASSES WHEN CUTTING AND CLEANING UP PARTS!

3. Check truss rod fit

Insert the rod into the bout and neck. You don't need to go all the way, just make sure that the rod fits snugly with some pressure (**Figure 3**).

If the rod is just slightly loose, this could result in warp over time, but I recommend moving forward without reprinting. You could try using a bit of epoxy to secure the rod.

If the rod is too tight (takes a hammer to install), you risk cracking the parts — I've done it! You can drill out the nut area (top of neck) to make sure it won't crack. If you're unable to insert the rod at all, try drilling out both parts.

NOTE: IF THE TRUSS ROD HOLE ON YOUR PART IS TOO SMALL OR TOO LARGE, IT MAY MEAN THAT YOU NEED TO PRINT NEW PARTS. IT'S GOOD TO CHECK THIS EARLY IN THE ASSEMBLY PROCESS.

4. Clean and deburr parts

Wearing your safety glasses, use a flat file, deburring tool, and X-Acto knife to clean any rafts or support material (if used) off the printed parts. Don't worry about getting the neck totally smooth, you'll work on that later. If your printer is dialed, you may not need to do much cleaning.

Carefully clean support material out of the amp plug area and remove any drooping strands of plastic (**Figure 4**).

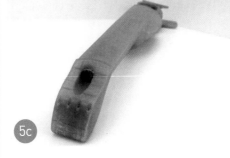

5. Install the truss rod

Install the rod into the bout of the instrument until it stops (**Figures 5a** and **5b**). This is the hardest part of the build!

Then, connect the bout and neck parts together with the rod. The rod should extend to the nut (the ridge at the top of the neck). A little long or short will be OK (**Figure 5c**).

6. Fasten the bout and neck

Due to part warp during printing, the neck and bout parts may not meet perfectly (**Figure 6a**). This is OK.

Insert the four 8-32 nuts into their slots, then poke them all the way down

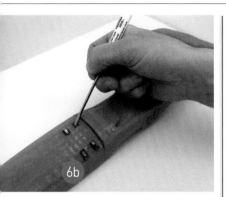

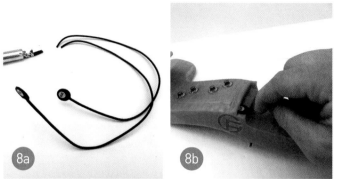

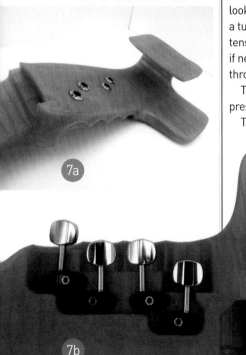

with a small screwdriver (**Figure 6b**).

Insert the socket head cap screws — 1½" screws in the topside, 1" screws on the bottom — and tighten until just barely snug.

Then very carefully turn them as tight as you can comfortably get with the short end of the Allen wrench. You should hear the plastic creaking, but not breaking or cracking (**Figure 6c**).

Now the bout and the neck should be contacting evenly!

> **TIP:**
> TIGHTEN THE SCREWS IN AN X PATTERN. THIS HELPS ENSURE THAT THE FASTENERS TIGHTEN EVENLY AND SECURELY.

7. Install machine heads (tuners)

The F-F-Fiddle CAD includes counterbored holes for the Gotoh Stealth tuner guides. These inserts aren't functionally necessary, but they look nicer, and they may protect the plastic if a tuner becomes loose over time due to string tension. Drill out the counterbore with the ⁵⁄₁₆" bit if necessary, but be careful not to go all the way through.

The guides should insert with strong finger pressure (**Figure 7a**).

These machine heads come in a pack of 6, 3 designed for mounting on the right side of a guitar and 3 for the left. They've been designed to fit efficiently and to allow you to tighten all strings with clockwise rotation of the knobs.

You'll use 2 right-hand and 2 left-hand tuners. Test-fit them as shown (**Figure 7b**), taking note of the correct orientation of the tuning knobs relative to the bodies. Take them all

out, remembering the orientation.

Now install the machine heads one at a time with the included screws. Get both screws started and screwed in about halfway. Then tighten them carefully and evenly until they're snug and there's no play between the tuner and the bout. Double-check the orientation of your tuners.

8. Prepare the pickups

Whether you have the internal or external K-Spot Twin pickups, you'll need to cut off the provided plug. Unthread and remove the plastic casing (for the external type) and cut the wires off about ½" above the solder joint (**Figure 8a**). Set the old plug aside, you may want to refer to it later.

Test-fit the pickups to see that they lie flat in their homes on the bout (**Figure 8b**). Clean up the area with a small file and knife if necessary.

9. Install pickups

Clean up the bridge area using a file and X-Acto knife. The bridge needs to rest only on the piezo pickups.

Install the pickups by threading their wires through the internal routing channel. They'll exit by the plug pocket (**Figure 9**).

10. Solder the audio plug

Cut the protruding pickup wires to about 3" long and carefully strip about 1" of the outer sheath. Try to avoid cutting any of the fine copper grounding wires.

Then strip the white-sheathed wires (conductors) about ½" back. Twist the conductors together, and twist the grounding wires together. Pass everything through a piece of large-diameter heat-shrink tubing (**Figure 10a**).

Pass a piece of small-diameter heat shrink over the grounding wires; this will act as a sheath to protect them. Wrap a large-diameter piece of heat-shrink over the first piece; this will cover the tab on the audio plug. Add a similar larger piece

10a

10b

10c

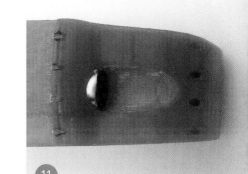

10d

11

over the conductor wires (**Figure 10b**).

The audio plug has 2 tabs. Solder the conductor wires to the tab that's sandwiched between the nonconductive layers. Then solder the grounding wires to the other tab. (If you're unsure, take a look at the plug you previously cut off.) Insulate the connections with the heat-shrink tubing (**Figure 10c**).

Tuck the plug into its pocket in the bout as shown. Tighten the hex nut as best you can — it's an awkward combination of rotating the plug and holding the nut with pliers or a small screwdriver (**Figure 10d**) and it needs improvement!

11. Neck detailing

Now's the time to sand down your neck if you'd like to. I've played both sanded and unsanded necks — sanded is better. For dark parts, clean thoroughly after sanding, and perhaps even use a small amount of vegetable oil to restore the part's luster.

File light but definite marks on the nut for your strings (**Figure 11**). The G and E strings should be 16mm apart, with the A and D strings positioned evenly between. I like to mark the positions with a Sharpie before I file. File lightly! If you file too far, you may need to add some epoxy and start over in order to build an instrument that feels right.

12. Install strings

Violin strings are color coded: here we have (from thick to thin) red for G, yellow for D, black for A, and green for E. Thread the strings through the neck of the instrument, so that the ball ends rest against the neck. Take care with the E string; if it sticks, blunt the tip by doubling it over (**Figure 12**).

12

IMPORTANT: PAY CLOSE ATTENTION TO THE DIRECTION OF THE WRAP OF EACH STRING — IT ALTERNATES. THIS ALLOWS A CLOCKWISE TURN ON ANY TUNING PEG TO TIGHTEN ITS STRING. I HAVE THE HARDEST TIME GETTING THIS RIGHT THE FIRST TIME — SO DON'T WORRY IF IT TAKES A FEW TRIES!

TO INSTALL A STRING:

A. Pass the covered end of the string through the hole in the tuner. Allow enough slack in the string to get at least 2 complete turns around the tuner.

B. Working with the main section of the string, not the tag end, pass the string around the tuner to make the first wrap, sending it over the tag end.

C. For the second wrap, cross over the first wrap and pass the string below the tag end. Crossing over ensures that the string's tension will lock it in place.

D. Now it should be too tight to wrap by hand. Turn the tuning peg clockwise to tighten the string. Tighten until lightly snug, so the string won't unwrap.

13a

13b

14

3 Fun Things to 3D Print
Written by Eric Chu

1

2

3

13. Install the bridge

Slide the bridge in underneath the strings (**Figure 13a**). Ensure that it rests properly on the 2 pickups and that the pickups seat properly in their pockets.

Lay the strings across the bridge. Space them evenly across a 34mm span (**Figure 13b**).

Like you did at the nut, lightly file a groove into the bridge to locate each string.

14. Tuning

Tune it up (**Figure 14**). Tighten all the strings together, don't tune them one at a time. Increase tension by turning the pegs slowly. If you tighten too quickly strings may slip or break.

As you tune the instrument, you'll notice that the tension on one string significantly influences the tension on the others. Because this instrument flexes more than a wooden violin, this effect is more pronounced.

Once the instrument is tuned and everything is looking good, trim off those tag ends, plug it in, and go learn some tunes! ◈

See more photos and video, and share your mods at makezine.com/fffiddle
Share it: *#makeprojects*

1. Fully Printable PCB Vise
by LeFabShop

thingiverse.com/thing:21357

This ball-joint vise rotates and holds PCBs for soldering. All parts are printed — requires no additional hardware to make!

2. Cooling Fan Replacement Blades
by CreativeTools

thingiverse.com/thing:186979

Broken fan blades on your 3D printer are a real nuisance. Instead of replacing the whole fan, remove the blades and print new ones that also add color to your printer.

3. Two Compartment Swivel Case
by Walter

thingiverse.com/thing:321827

This stylish little organizer prints in three parts and friction-fits together, no fasteners needed. Good for securely storing small parts like screws, beads, and resistors.

The Zip Tie Lounge Chair

Written by Will Holman

Transform 44 cable fasteners and a half-sheet of plywood into a streamlined lounge chair that's perfect for the nomadic maker.

Will Holman

Time Required:
A Few Hours
Cost:
Less Than $50

WILL HOLMAN
(objectguerilla.com) is a designer, craftsman, and a fellow at the Robert W. Deutsch Foundation, working to bring the new maker economy to Baltimore. He's writing a book on making furniture from salvaged materials.

Materials
» **Plywood, ¾", 4'×4'**
» **Cable ties (44)** aka zip ties, 50lb breaking strength
» **Wood finish**

Tools
» **CNC router** minimum 4'×4' bed size
» **¼" upcut endmill**
» **Pull saw**
» **Orbital sander**
» **Sanding block**

THE ICONIC STEAM-BENT CHAIR NO. 14, INVENTED BY MICHAEL THONET IN 1859, was the first flat-pack furniture kit. It was shipped across Europe on then-new railways, becoming one of the most popular chairs ever made.

CNC manufacturing gives us the ability to do Mr. Thonet one better, distributing the *information* about the chair instead of the chair itself. Using new digital tools, I spent 6 months designing and prototyping the Zip Tie Lounge Chair, a low-key living room companion for makers on the move. It goes together (and comes apart) in minutes and costs less than $50.

1. **Prepare files.** Download the files and assembly instructions from OpenDesk (opendesk. cc/designers/will-holman), and translate the DXF drawing into toolpaths using your favorite CAM program. The toolpath order, as seen in the drawing, should be:
» **Green:** Drilling toolpath
» **Cyan:** Pocket toolpath, cut on the vector, ³/₁₆" deep
» **Red:** Profile toolpath, cut through the material on the outside of the vector. Add at least 3 tabs per piece to hold parts in place.

2. **Cut.** Secure the plywood to the spoil board with screws. Note that there's a 1¼" border built into the file for screw clearance. Choose your tooling. I used a ¼" upcut endmill. Home the x and y axes, then calibrate the z-height. Run the toolpaths.

3. **Finish.** Cut through the tabs with a pull saw. Sand the faces with an orbital sander and ease the edges with a sanding block. Apply finish of your choice — I used butcher block oil and citrus-based wax for an Earth-friendly shine.

4. **Assemble.** Fasten the arms to the side frames by feeding zip ties through the matching holes and pulling tight. Secure the sides to the front and back frames, forming a box.

Hitch the 3 seat panels together in order of descending size, without tightening the zip ties all the way, to form a flexible "hammock."

Attach the seat to the base through the middle of the first and last seat panels. This is a bit tricky; it helps to lay the chair frame on its side so you don't have to support the weight as you attempt to tighten the zip ties. Then snip off the tails of the zip ties. Add a thin cushion made from closed-cell foam camping pads for extra comfort. ⊘

See assembly diagrams and more photos at makezine.com/zip-tie-chair
Share it: *#makeprojects*

PROJECTS

Gunther Kirsch

Face Recognition Treasure Safe

Use a Raspberry Pi, camera, and free software to make a lockbox that opens only when it sees your mug. Written and photographed by Tony DiCola and David Scheltema

TONY DICOLA
is an engineer who works at Adafruit Industries and has a passion for making things that use Arduino, Raspberry Pi, and other embedded platforms.

DAVID SCHELTEMA
loves to tinker and write about electronics. His days are spent building projects and working as a technical editor for *Make:*.

PROTECT YOUR VALUABLES FROM PRYING EYES WITHOUT REMEMBERING A COMBINA-TION OR CARRYING A KEY. Your face is the key to unlock this safe!

This project will show you how to use *face recognition*, a computer vision technique used by security firms and governments that's now available to the DIYer. The software is based on algorithms provided by the OpenCV computer vision library. The Raspberry Pi is a perfect platform because it has the power to run OpenCV, and it's small enough to fit almost anywhere.

You'll modify a toy safe with a servo to turn the tumblers, then program the Pi with "mug shots" of yourself, or other faces to admit — or deny.

1. Mount the Pi on the door
Drill ⅛" holes and mount the Pi with machine screws, standoffs, and nuts (**Figure 1**).

2. Attach the servo horn
Bend or cut the tabs on the 2 lock tumblers so they spin freely. Cut the arms off a servo horn and hot-glue it to the center of the lock.

3. Make the servo bracket
Cut a strip of sheet metal about 1½"×8" and cut out a rectangle in the center that matches the face of your servo. Clean up edges with a file.

Test-fit your servo into the bracket and the servo horn. Bend the bracket so it fits neatly around the lock. Drill a ⅛" hole at each end.

4. Mount the servo
Mark the bracket hole locations on the door, and drill ⅛" holes. Drill four ⅛" holes in the bracket and use zip ties to secure the servo (**Figure 4**). Then rivet the servo bracket to the safe door.

5. Install the camera and button
Drill a ¼" hole in the door and enlarge it with a square file so the camera lens fits (**Figure 5**). Mount the camera board using double-sided tape. Drill a ½" hole and mount the pushbutton.

6. Connect the electronics
Solder male header pins and a 10K resistor to a small circular perf board (**Figure 6**), following the schematic on the project page at makezine.com/projects/face-recognition-treasure-safe.

Connect the servo's signal line to GPIO pin 18 on the Pi. Connect the servo's power and ground to the battery holder's power and ground.

Connect one lead of the pushbutton to GPIO 25, and through the 10K resistor to the Pi's 3.3V power pin. Connect the other button lead to Pi ground. Connect the battery ground to Pi ground.

Time Required:
2-4 Hours
Cost:
$100-$130

Materials

» **Raspberry Pi Model B single-board computer** Maker Shed item #MKRPI2, makershed.com
» **Raspberry Pi Camera Module** Maker Shed #MKRPI3
» **Toy safe** We used the Schylling Steel Safe with Alarm, Amazon #B003D0EM62, about 9"×8"×6".
» **Servomotor** Maker Shed #MKPX17
» **Battery holder, 4xAAA**
» **Switch, momentary push-button**
» **Resistor, 10kΩ ¼W**
» **Perf board**
» **Male header pins (11)**
» **Jumper wires, female-to-female** Maker Shed #MKKN4
» **Scrap of sheet metal** about 2"×8"
» **Machine screws, #6-32"×¾" with nuts (2)**
» **Standoffs, ⅛" ID × ½"** You can cut them from an old ballpoint pen.
» **Zip ties**

Tools

» **Drill and drill bits**
» **Soldering iron and solder**
» **Tinsnips**
» **Vise**
» **Hammer**
» **Chisel or high-speed rotary tool** such as a Dremel
» **Center punch**
» **File**
» **Screwdriver**
» **Pop rivet gun with aluminum rivets, ⅛"×³⁄₁₆"**

7. Route the USB cable
Drill a hole on the rear bottom corner of the safe, large enough to pass your Pi's USB cable.

8. Install software and enable camera
We've prepared a prebuilt image with all the programs installed. Download it from the project page, then go to elinux.org/RPi_Easy_SD_Card_Setup and follow the SD flashing guide for your computer's operating system: Windows, Linux, or OS X. (To get your hands dirty with a custom install, visit the project page for details.)

Run the command `sudo raspi-config`, select Enable Camera, and reboot.

9. Train the face recognition
In a terminal session on the Pi, navigate to the directory with the software and execute the command `sudo python capture-positives.py` to start the training script.

Press the button on the safe to take a picture with the camera. The script will attempt to detect a single face in the captured image and store it as a "positive" training image in the *./training/ positive* subdirectory. This will train the "classifier" function of the software to recognize your face. Use the button to capture 5 or more images of your face from different angles and with differ-

TIP: VIEW THE FILE *CAPTURE.PGM* IN A GRAPHICS EDITOR TO SEE WHAT THE PI CAMERA IS PICKING UP, AND CHECK OUT THE *./TRAINING/NEGATIVE* DIRECTORY TO SEE EXAMPLES (FROM AN AT&T FACE RECOGNITION DATABASE) OF PEOPLE WHO ARE *NOT* ALLOWED TO OPEN THE SAFE.

ent lighting (**Figure 9**).

Finally, run the command `python train. py` to process the positive and negative training images and train the face recognition algorithm. This takes about 10 minutes.

10. Configure the servo
Run the command `sudo python servo.py` and enter different pulse-width values (from **1000** to **2000**) to determine which values move the servo latch into a locked and unlocked position on your safe. Then edit *config.py* and set the `LOCK_SERVO_UNLOCKED` and `LOCK_SERVO_LOCKED` values accordingly.

11. Run your smart safe!
Finally, execute the command `sudo python box.py` and your safe will lock itself and wait for the button to be pressed, then grab a camera image and try to recognize the face of the user. If it matches, it will unlock itself. Press the button again to lock the safe and repeat the process.

Troubleshooting
If the face recognition isn't working well, you can either take more positive training images and train it again, or tweak the `POSITIVE_THRESHOLD` to a higher value in the *config.py* file to make it less sensitive.

If you ever need to force the safe to unlock, just run *servo.py* again and input the unlocked servo position. ●

Get the code and schematic at makezine.com/projects/face-recognition-treasure-safe.

Share it: *#makeprojects*

Vinyl Digitizer Phono Preamp

Convert LPs and 45s to sound files and take your music into the future.

Written by Ross Hershberger ■ Photographed by Jeffrey Braverman

Time Required:
1-2 Hours
Cost:
$50-$70

ROSS HERSHBERGER
has worked as a mainframe programmer, tooling machinist, restorer of vintage tube amps, custodial equipment technician, and several other unlikely jobs. Since 2012, he has worked as a YAG Laser Field Service Engineer for the North American division of Trumpf GmbH. His Bass Bump Headphone Amp was featured in *Make:* Volume 37.

YOU'VE PROBABLY STUMBLED ACROSS AMAZING VINYL LPS at a friend's house, yard sale, or record store, but reluctantly passed them up, because in our mobile digital wireless world, vinyl records are about as convenient as a telephone attached to the wall. Next time don't pass them up, snap them up. With the Vinyl Digitizer Phono Preamp, you can "dub" records onto your computer and convert the sound files for your phone, MP3 player, car, or anywhere else you need music.

The system consists of 5 parts: your record turntable, the Vinyl Digitizer Phono Preamp that we'll show you how to build, the Diamond Audio USB interface, your computer, and Audacity software. I designed the preamp to do three things: Amplify the tiny signal from the turntable's phono cartridge, apply a frequency equalization specifically for vinyl records called the RIAA playback curve, and optimize the gain (volume amplification) to be compatible with the Diamond USB sound card. From there, the sound card converts the input signal to a digital data stream, and the

Audacity software nimbly turns those old 45s, 78s, and LPs into new MP3s (or the digital audio format of your choice).

Why should you care about a dead medium like records anyway? Because as an inquisitive person you're susceptible to having your mind blown by what's on them. Fifty-plus years of Gilbert and Sullivan, opera, rockabilly, Delta blues, prog rock, Lenny Bruce, Beethoven, Balinese gamelan, jug bands, "Yardbird" Parker, klezmer, and much more that you can't even imagine. Long playing records were the primary format for music distribution for the second half of the 20th century, a tremendous time for musical creativity and performance. They were produced by the hundreds of millions. From *Bozo Under the Sea* to Van Cliburn at the Tchaikovsky Competition, it's all still out there and much of this material never made the transition to digital.

Here's how to build the Vinyl Digitizer Phono Preamp and bring your discoveries into the future with you.

1. Prepare the circuit board

You'll assemble the preamp circuit on a RadioShack printed circuit board. But first, label the PCB hole positions to help you place the components.

Use a fine-tipped marker to number the traces on the copper side of the board (the bottom), as shown, before installing components.

Flip the board over to the component side (the top) and number the traces to match.

Label the 5 holes of each trace with letters A through E, with A at the center of the board and E at the outside. Thus the inner hole on the trace at the upper left is 1A and the outer hole of the trace at the upper right is 20E (**Figure A**). Hole 16E will have 2 wires in it. Widen the hole with a small file or drill to approximately 1.5 times its width. Be careful not to remove all of the copper from the hole on the solder side.

2. Mark and drill the enclosure

Cover one long face of the box and the short side to the left of it with masking tape. Also tape the inside surface of the bottom cover of the box. Measure and mark the positions for the drill holes in the box, as shown in **Figures B–D**. The bottom of the box will hold the circuit board. Place the circuit board against the right edge, centered vertically, and mark the upper left and lower right hole positions (**Figure B**).

Drill all the holes. You can use a ⅛" drill bit for the 3mm holes.

NOTE: THE 3MM HOLE ON THE FRONT OF THE BOX IS FOR AN OPTIONAL POWER INDICATOR LED. I HAVE DELETED THIS LED HERE, AS IT CAN SHORTEN BATTERY LIFE BY 50%. THE SWITCH POSITION WILL INDICATE IF THE UNIT IS TURNED ON (UP).

3. Install the RCA input jacks

Bend the tab of each grounding washer at a 30° angle to the ring (**Figure E**). Strip a 3" length of bare 24ga solid-core wire, and solder a ground washer tab to each end (**Figure F**).

Wrap the center of the wire around the #4 × 1" screw and tighten a nut to hold the wire against the head.

Pass the screw through the 3mm hole on the end of the box from the inside and nut it tightly on the outside. Place two #4 washers on the screw and another nut, loosely.

If the RCA jacks are color coded, place the red one on the right and black on the left, as viewed upright from the outside (shown upside down here). Pass the RCA jacks through the jack holes from the outside. Place one ground ring on each jack inside the box and nut both jacks tightly (**Figure G**).

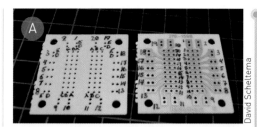
A

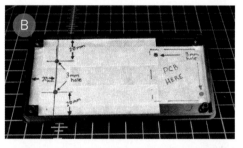
B

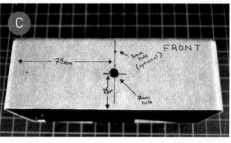
C

D

E

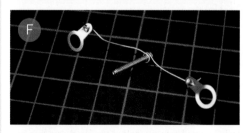
F

G

David Scheltema

Materials

- » **Digital 7.1 USB External Sound Card, Diamond model XS71U** RadioShack #55071954
- » **Project enclosure, 6"×3"×2"** RadioShack #270-1805
- » **Perf board** RadioShack #276-159
- » **IC socket, 8-pin** RadioShack #276-1995
- » **Battery holders, 9V (2)** RadioShack #270-326
- » **Capacitors, 0.1µF 50V 10% (2)** RadioShack #272-1069
- » **Phono plug, ⅛" stereo** RadioShack #274-284
- » **Switch, DPDT toggle** RadioShack #275-614
- » **Op-amp IC chip, TL082/TL-082CP Wide Dual JFET Input** RadioShack #276-1715
- » **Capacitors, Mylar, 0.47µF 100V (2)** RadioShack #55046808
- » **Battery clips, 9V (2)** RadioShack #270-324
- » **Capacitors, Mylar, 0.033µF 50V (4)** RadioShack #55046782. Look for code "333" on the body, meaning 33,000pF (33 plus 3 zeros) which equals 0.033µF.
- » **Capacitors, ceramic, 330pF 50V (2)** Radio Shack #55047538
- » **Resistors, ⅛W: 47kΩ (2), 82kΩ (2), 3kΩ (1), 1kΩ (2), 5.1kΩ (2), and 18kΩ (2)** from Radio Shack assortment #271-003
- » **Machine screws, #4-40: ¼" (2), 3/16" (2), and 1" (1)**
- » **Flat washers, #4 (2)**
- » **Nuts, #4-40 (7)**
- » **RCA phono jacks (2)** RadioShack #274-852
- » **Batteries, 9V (2)** RadioShack #230-2211
- » **Velcro tape (optional)**

Tools

- » **Soldering iron and solder**
- » **Small screwdrivers**
- » **Tweezers**
- » **Wire stripper/cutter**
- » **Fingernail clipper**
- » **Magnifier (optional)**
- » **Utility knife**
- » **Drill with ⅛" and 7mm bits**
- » **Hacksaw blade**
- » **Pliers, mini long-nose**
- » **Digital multimeter**
- » **Ruler, metric**
- » **Fine-point marker**
- » **Masking tape**
- » **Hot glue gun**
- » **Turntable**
- » **Computer with Audacity software and manual** free downloads from audacity.sourceforge.net

4. Build the PCB

Assemble the circuit board following the schematic (**Figure H**) and step-by-step instructions at makezine.com/vinyl-digitizer-phono-preamp. The schematic shows one channel; build 2 (**Figure I**).

5. Solder the output wires to the plug

Remove the plastic housing from the ⅛" phono plug and slide it down the orange white/blue/brown wire bundle.

Using a multimeter, determine which solder tabs on the plug connect to the tip of the plug (left signal), the ring of the plug (right signal) and the body of the plug (signal ground). Solder the orange white wire (left output) to the solder tab for the tip, the blue wire (right output) to the solder tab for the ring, and the brown wire (output ground) to the solder tab for the body.

Gently crimp the ground bar's tabs around the wire bundle, making sure not to cut the insulation and cause a short (**Figure J**). Use a multimeter to check for short circuits between ground/ring and ground/tip. The correct resistance reading is 47,000 ohms (47kΩ). Install the plastic housing on the plug.

6. Connect the input wires to the RCA jacks

Solder the green wire of the green/orange white/orange bundle to the right (red) jack signal tab. Solder the orange wire to the left (black) jack signal tab, and the orange white wire to the bare wire loop between the ground lugs. Bend the bare wire loops against the wall of the box so they won't cause shorts (**Figure K**).

7. Install the power switch

The power switch has 3 pairs of solder tabs, but we'll use only 2 of the pairs, which I've numbered 1 through 4, including the central pair (3,4). Solder the twisted red and black pair of power wires from the PCB to switch terminals 3 and 4 respectively. When stripping these 2 wires,

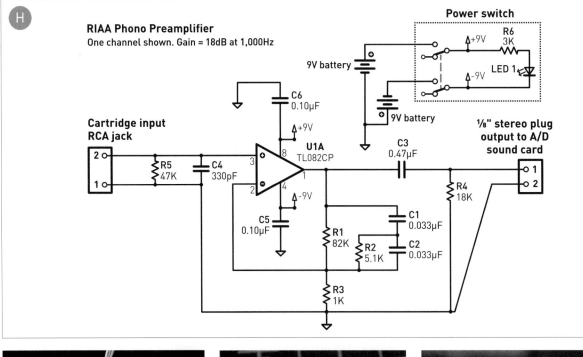

H

RIAA Phono Preamplifier
One channel shown. Gain = 18dB at 1,000Hz

Power switch

R6 3K

9V battery

LED 1

C6 0.10µF

+9V

Cartridge input RCA jack

⅛" stereo plug output to A/D sound card

U1A
TL082CP

9V battery

C3 0.47µF

R5 47K
C4 330pF

3
8
1
2
4
-9V

R4 18K

1
2

C5 0.10µF

R1 82K
R2 5.1K

C1 0.033µF
C2 0.033µF

R3 1K

Damien Scogin

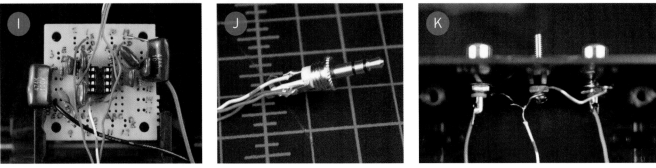

I J K

L

M

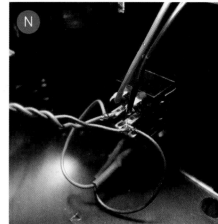

N

leave 3mm of bare wire exposed when they're soldered on (**Figure L**).

Solder the red wire from a battery clip to terminal 1 on the power switch as shown. Solder the black battery clip wire to terminal 2 (**Figure M**). Install the power switch inside the project box, so that its 2 unused solder tabs are nearest the top of the box, and terminals 1 and 2 (battery clip wires) are nearest the open bottom of the box (**Figure N**). Tighten the switch's nut on the outside.

8. Final assembly

Insert the TL082CP IC chip into the socket. The notch in the chip body orients toward the end of the board with PCB rows 1 and 20. This places the 'pin 1' indicator dot on the chip body at PCB hole 4A. Take standard antistatic precautions with the chip, as its input JFETs could be damaged by a static discharge: Leave it in its conductive foam until you're ready to install it, then touch a metal object to discharge any static before handling the chip, and keep yourself grounded while handling it.

Install the two 9V battery holders on the box bottom with #4 × ³/₁₆" screws and nuts as shown. Pass the screw through from the outside so the nut is on the inside. Using #4 × ¼" screws and nuts, attach the PCB to the bottom of the box in the orientation shown. Do not overtighten the screws or the PCB could be damaged.

Place a pair of fresh 9V batteries in the clips and slide them toward the near end of the box bottom. Orient the batteries so their terminals are nearest the PCB and positive terminal is closest to the bottom of the box (**Figure O**). You should use 2 new 9V batteries of the same type so that they discharge at the same time.

Turn the power switch off (down) and snap the battery connectors onto the battery terminals. Close up the box, carefully moving the wires around as needed for clearance. Pass the output wire/plug through the slot at the front of the box (**Figure P**).

Install the 4 Phillips screws in the bottom of the

box. I stuck 4 rubber feet on the bottom of mine to help it stay in place when hooked to cables.

9. Hook it up and digitize

Set the Diamond Audio USB External Sound Card on top of your Vinyl Digitizer Phono Preamp and plug the preamp's output plug into the sound card's Line-In jack. Velcro tape would handy here.

Using the supplied USB A/B cable, connect the Diamond sound card to the computer. It should appear as External USB Sound Card or similar name.

Plug the turntable's left and right output plugs into the input jacks of the Vinyl Digitizer Phono Preamp. **IMPORTANT:** If your turntable has a ground lead, securely connect it between the washers on the screw between the input jacks. Without it, there will be buzzing noise along with the audio.

Start the Audacity software and select the external USB audio device as the input. Follow the Audacity manual's "Sample Workflow for LP Digitization" to record and save records. It's easy! ◐

Get step-by-step instructions for building the PCB, details on how the circuit and preamp system work, and more about turntables and records at
makezine.com/vinyl-digitizer-phono-preamp
Share it: **#makeprojects**

O

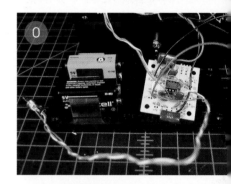

P

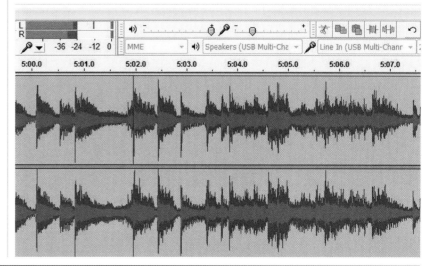

Brew a Vintage IPA

Re-create the dry, highly hopped ale that quenched the British Empire.

Written by Ronald Pattinson

**Time Required:
An Afternoon
Cost:
$25–$40**

RONALD PATTINSON
is a brewing historian, member of the British Guild of Beer Writers, and author of the blog Shut Up About Barclay Perkins. Beeradvocate.com calls him "one of the finest and most illuminating beer historians," and he has collaborated on new batches of old beers with a variety of beer bloggers and craft brewers. He is based in Amsterdam.

Materials

» **Pale malt, 2 row, 13.25lbs**
» **Hops, East Kent Golding, fresh, 13oz** not wet, just fresh
» **Water**
» **Yeast, Wyeast 1098 British Ale — dry**
» **Yeast, Wyeast 1099 Whitbread Ale**
» **Yeast, Brettanomyces clausenii (optional)**
» **Sugar** for priming bottles

Tools

» **Brew kettle, 8gal or bigger** stainless steel or aluminum
» **Wort chiller (optional)**
» **Mash tun or muslin bag, 10gal** Make a DIY mash tun from a 10gal Igloo cooler, or use the "brew-in-a-bag" method instead.
» **Large spoon or aeration wand**
» **Glass carboy, 6gal or bigger**
» **Airlock and rubber stopper**
» **Racking cane and siphon tube**
» **Sanitizer**
» **Bottle capper and caps**
» **Bottles, clean**

THE STORY OF IPA IS ONE OF THE MOST ROMANTIC IN BREWING HISTORY — but much of it isn't true. The first pale ales were exported to India in the late 18th century, and a London brewery called Hodgson was able to establish a near monopoly in the trade. Hodgson was canny enough to let the East India Company's ships have beer on extended credit. After Hodgson began to demand cash up front, three brewers in Burton-upon-Trent — Allsopp, Bass, and Salt — began shipping the newfangled beer in 1823. The British expats loved it.

The beer they exported had several defining characteristics: It was very pale, brewed from only the highest-quality and palest malt. It was heavily hopped, both in the kettle and in the form of dry hops. And it was extremely highly attenuated. This was vital to stop the beer from bursting its casks or becoming infected on the long, hot journey to India. With nearly all the sugars

fermented out, there was nothing for any bacteria to eat.

The one thing IPA wasn't was strong, at least not by the standards of the day. Exports were about 7% alcohol by volume, and domestic IPAs closer to 6% — comparable to mild ales and porters.

How did IPA come to be sold back home in Britain? The tale usually told is of a ship bound for India that was wrecked in the Irish Channel. Its cargo was salvaged and sold in Liverpool, where it was a sensation. There's just one problem. No record exists of such a shipwreck. More likely, demand was created by officers returning from India who had got a taste of IPA.

1839 Reid IPA

Reid & Co. brewed several pale ales in the 1830s, and this IPA is a real cracker. It's a typical early 19th-century recipe — just pale malt and lots of Goldings — but all of the hops were fresh. It's still recognizable today as an

IPA, but with a unique character and hop flavor unlike any modern version.

I've adapted the recipe to a single-mash, single-sparge scheme for homebrewing. Attenuation is about 67% at the time of racking, but IPA was aged in casks for months before even getting on a ship — plenty of time for *Brettanomyces clausenii* to bring the gravity down and push attenuation up toward 85%. For historical accuracy, the longer you leave it in secondary fermentation the better.

FOR 6 GALLONS OF ALE:

» Pale malt 2 row — 13.25lbs
» Golding 90 min — 5.00oz (142g)
» Golding 60 min — 4.00oz (113g)
» Golding 30 min — 4.00oz (113g)
» OG — 1057
» FG — 1019
» ABV — 5.03
» Apparent attenuation — 66.7% (racking)
» IBUs — 177
» SRM (color) — 5
» Mash at — 157°F (69.4°C)
» Sparge at — 175°F (79.4°C)
» Boil time — 90 min
» Pitching temp — 61°F (16.1°C)
» Yeast —
Wyeast 1098 British Ale — dry
Wyeast 1099 Whitbread Ale
(optional) Brettanomyces clausenii

This article is adapted from The Home Brewer's Guide to Vintage Beer *(Quarry Books, 2014).* ◉

Read more brewing tips and trade tasting notes at makezine.com/vintage-IPA
Share it: **#makeprojects**

Etch a Kettle with a 9V Battery
Use a knife-maker's trick to safely, permanently mark stainless steel or aluminum. Written by Matt Bates

Gunther Kirsch

Time Required: 1 Hour
Cost: $1-$5

MATT BATES
has been homebrewing for 10 years and has enjoyed making his own tools and equipment for the hobby for just as long.

Materials
» **Brew kettle, stainless steel or aluminum**
» **Vinegar**
» **Salt**
» **Battery, 9V**
» **Battery snap connector, 9V, with leads**
» **Tape, water resistant such as vinyl electrical tape**
» **Cotton swab**
» **Adhesive stencils of numbers, from a craft store**
» **Disposable gloves**

6

AS A HOMEBREWER I NEED TO MEASURE MY KETTLE VOLUMES at various stages during the brew day — but my kettle had no volume markings. So I researched metal etching and came across a technique used by knife makers to brand their knives: *electrolytic acid etching*. You'll use vinegar for the acid. The vinegar needs to be conductive, so you'll add an electrolyte: table salt. A power source of 9 to 12 volts DC will leave a frosty white mark that's permanent.

1. Mark the water levels. Level your kettle and fill it, in the increments you wish to mark. Mark each water level as you go. Apply tape to create bar-shaped stencils.

2. Apply number stencils.

3. Combine vinegar and salt.

4. Hook up the kettle. Tape the bare end of the 9V battery snap's positive (+) lead to your kettle. This will electrify your entire kettle with a very low voltage.

5. Prepare your etching tool. Twist the bare end of the battery snap's negative (–) lead tightly around the head of the cotton swab.

6. Etch. Dip the swab in the vinegar solution and touch it to the kettle at your first mark. If you hear sizzling or see bubbling, it's working. It only takes a few seconds of contact to permanently dissolve some metal, so keep the swab moving.

Rinse your first couple of marks and check your work. When all markings are etched to your satisfaction, disconnect the battery, pull the stencils off, and rinse thoroughly. ◉

For more tips and photos, go to makezine.com/etch-a-kettle
Share it: **#makeprojects**

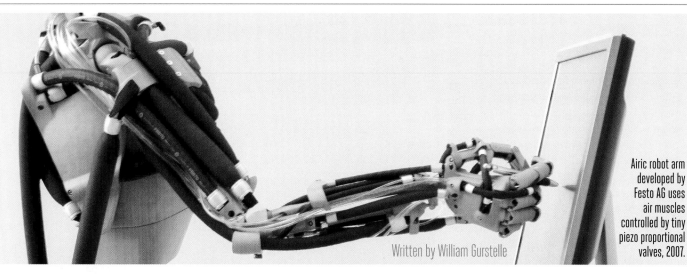

Airic robot arm developed by Festo AG uses air muscles controlled by tiny piezo proportional valves, 2007.

Written by William Gurstelle

WILLIAM GURSTELLE is a contributing editor of *Make:* magazine. His new book, *Defending Your Castle: Build Catapults, Crossbows, Moats and More* is now available.

Materials

» **Soft silicone rubber tubing,** ⅜" OD, ¼" ID, 8" length
» **Hard-sided polyethylene (HDPE) tubing,** ⅜" OD, ¼" ID, 24"–36" length
» **Expandable braided polyester sleeve,** ½" ID, 8" length commonly used by electricians to bundle wires and cables, such as McMaster-Carr #9284K4, mcmaster.com
» **Nylon bolt,** ¼-20
» **Miniature PVC ball valve, 3-port, with ¼" barbed connectors** such as McMaster #4757K57
» **Hose clamps,** size #04 (4)
» **Adapter fitting,** ¼" NPTF male thread to ¼" barbed connector McMaster #5372K112
» **Quick-connect air hose coupling,** ¼" plug with ¼" NPTF female end McMaster #6534K56 aka industrial interchange coupling

Tools

» **Scissors**
» **Screwdriver**
» **Air compressor or other source of high-pressure air**
» **Teflon tape**
» **Safety glasses**

Joseph McKibben and the Air Muscle

A father's love inspired this A-bomb maker to invent a pneumatic actuator that's used in robots today.

ENGINEERS AND SCIENTISTS OFTEN CREATE WONDERFUL, CONSTRUCTIVE DEVICES THAT MAKE LIFE BETTER for people who are sick and disabled. Nearly as often, they design and build weapons and implements of warfare. And once in a while, the same person does both.

Joseph Laws McKibben was an important figure in World War II's Manhattan Project. A nuclear physicist from the University of Wisconsin, Dr. McKibben was on the team that researched the properties of the tamper, the device that controlled the speed and power of the atomic bomb's chain reaction.

In addition to being a theoretician, McKibben was a hands-on sort of scientist. On July 16, 1945, he pushed the button that set off the first ever A-bomb — code-named Trinity — in the New Mexico desert. Early that morning, McKibben made the final electrical connections to the explosives that would initiate the chain reaction in the bomb. Then he hopped into his jeep and drove six miles to a concrete bunker where the countdown to H-Hour was underway. There, McKibben threw the switch to initiate the final control sequence that detonated the bomb (**Figure A**).

Six years later, in 1952, McKibben's daughter, Karan, was stricken with polio (**Figure B**). Paralyzed from the neck down, she was confined to an iron lung for a time. Dr. McKibben felt that he could use his engineering skills to improve the quality of her life. So, working with the doctors at the rehabilitation center where she was living, he began researching ways to give polio patients some control over their fingers.

McKibben studied the existing hydraulic, electric, and pneumatic methods of moving paralyzed arms, and he became intrigued by one that he felt had particular promise. A few years earlier, a German scientist had prototyped a clever pneumatic gadget operated by compressed gas. The device consisted of a flexible bladder that could be filled with carbon dioxide. The bulging bladder closely simulated the natural motion of human muscles. Could this idea, McKibben wondered, allow paralyzed fingers to work once again?

Within a few years McKibben's team developed the gadget now known as the air muscle, or braided pneumatic actuator. Dr. McKibben placed it next to his daughter's paralyzed forearm and attached it to her thumb and first and second fingers with splints. When she operated a lever by shrugging her shoulder, gas flowed into a tube, causing a contraction that drew the paralyzed fingers together. At the next touch of the lever, the plastic tube deflated and her fingers relaxed.

McKibben's air muscle has become an important component used by roboticists and biomedical engineers, thanks to its high force-to-weight ratio, flexible structure, and low manufacturing costs. A typical modern air muscle consists of a flexible rubber tube or bladder inside a polymer mesh sleeve that's braided in a helical weave. When the bladder is inflated, the mesh expands in width but simultaneously contracts in length. This shortens the muscle, so anything attached to the ends of the muscle is pulled together. The muscle contracts smoothly and with a surprising amount of pulling force.

You can easily construct an air muscle from hardware-store parts. It's a great example of using basic pneumatic principles to make devices for controlling motion. It's also a testament to Joe McKibben's versatile ability to engineer solutions to different sorts of problems.

Make an Air Muscle

1. Insert the bolt into one end of the silicone rubber tubing. It should fit snugly.

2. Insert the rubber tubing all the way through the braided sleeve. It may take quite a bit of wiggling.

3. Push the middle port of the barbed 3-way valve fitting into the open end of the rubber tubing as far as possible.

4. Place one hose clamp over the sleeve, tube, and barb, and tighten securely. Place the other hose clamp over the sleeve, tube, and bolt, and again, tighten securely so it is airtight. This completes the air muscle.

5. Now make your air line. Cut a 6" length of the polyethylene tubing. Insert one of the remaining barbed ports of the 3-way valve. If it's too tight, try warming the tubing in hot water first. Secure the connection with a hose clamp.

6. Insert the barb of the ¼" barbed to ¼" NPTF male connector into the other end of the polyethylene tube. Secure with a hose clamp.

7. Finally, connect the female end of the ¼" NPTF quick-connect hose coupling to the male end of the ¼" NPTF to barbed connector, using pipe compound or teflon tape between the male and female connectors. Your air muscle is now ready for use.

Use It

There are many ways to mount your air muscle. The easiest is to use wire to attach one end of the muscle to a support and the other end to something you want to move. By using levers and pul-

Festo AG & Co. KG

Time Required: 1 Hour
Cost: $20–$40

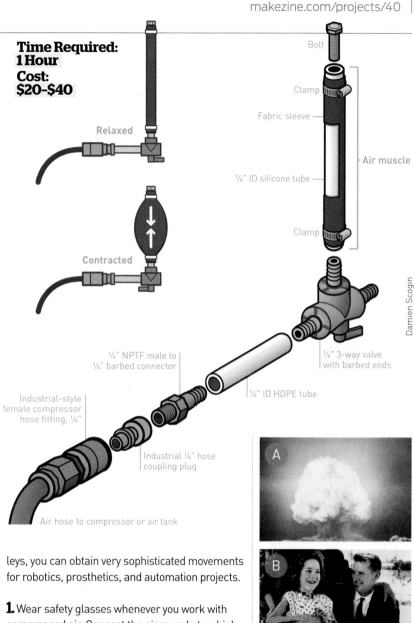

Relaxed

Contracted

Bolt

Clamp

Fabric sleeve

Air muscle

¼" ID silicone tube

Clamp

¼" NPTF male to ¼" barbed connector

Industrial-style female compressor hose fitting, ¼"

Industrial ¼" hose coupling plug

¼" ID HDPE tube

¼" 3-way valve with barbed ends

Air hose to compressor or air tank

Damien Scogin

leys, you can obtain very sophisticated movements for robotics, prosthetics, and automation projects.

1. Wear safety glasses whenever you work with compressed air. Connect the air muscle to a high-pressure air source such as a compressor or air tank. The higher the pressure, the more the air muscle will contract — but too much pressure may split the tube.

2. Connect your air source to the air hose coupling.

3. Open the 3-way valve so that the air muscle fills with air. As it fills, the rubber tube expands but is constrained by the mesh sleeve, causing the air muscle to contract. Moving the valve handle in the other direction exhausts the air from the muscle, allowing it to relax. ◉

See video and step-by-step photos, and share your air muscle mods at makezine.com/air-muscle.
Share it: **#makeprojects**

A

B

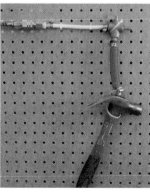

Globe Photos

Fond o' Bondo

An illustrated guide to the creative side of body filler.

Written by Larry Cotton and Phil Bowie

LARRY COTTON
is a semi-retired power-tool designer and part-time math instructor who loves music, computers, electronics, furniture design, birds, and his wife – not necessarily in that order.

PHIL BOWIE
is a lifelong freelance magazine writer with three suspense novels in print. He's on the web at philbowie.blogspot.com

Gunther Kirsch

Time Required:
1 Hour–A Weekend
Cost:
$20–$100

Materials
» **Container of body filler, including hardener, catalyst, or activator**
» **Lacquer thinner or acetone** for cleaning
» **Cooking spray ("Pam"), silicone spray, or WD-40** for release agent.

FOR FINISHING:
» **Glazing and spot putty** (primer filler)
» **Primer-surfacer**, such as gray Rustoleum or Krylon
» **Paint** (enamel, lacquer, or latex)

Tools
» **Formica**, small piece for mixing
» **Respirator**
» **Stanley Surform pocket plane**
» **Flat stick or large flat-blade screwdriver**
» **Artist's palette knife**
» **Latex gloves**
» **Files**
» **Sandpaper**, 60- to 400-grit
» **Wax paper** (optional)
» **Syringe, 20ml** (optional)

BODY FILLER IS A THICK, TWO-PART POLYESTER RESIN, COMMONLY CALLED BONDO.
Cursory Googling reveals a universe of mostly automotive applications, primarily for repairing body damage, but we'll leave that to the experts and show you a few creative uses for this versatile stuff.

We recommend 3M's Bondo 262 for general-purpose work, which comes with a tube of reddish-brown hardener. For tips on mixing and curing body filler, check out our Skill Builder (makezine. com/working-with-bondo), and Shawn Thorsson's awesome video tutorial (makezine.com/body-filler). Now let's get creative!

1. Custom tool grip
Slather mixed Bondo onto a prepared wooden tool handle; a hammer's a good place to start. Wearing a tight-fitting latex glove, grip the handle as you'll use it. When it sets enough to hold its shape (it will get warm, but not uncomfortably so), slowly release your grip and immediately remove

excess material with the Surform. After curing, Dremel, file, sand, and finish.

2. Casting
Do you have an antique candle holder, bookend, or prized earring, but have lost its twin? Need an antique drawer pull that's no longer available? Maybe you'd just like to duplicate an item you can't buy any more. Make a mold of the item using mold-building latex. (We used Castin' Craft's Mold Builder liquid latex rubber from Michael's.) Follow instructions on its container to build up the mold in layers, including a flange for support and filler containment, reinforcing if necessary with cotton gauze. Block any holes you won't need in the final part.

When the latex is dry, remove the item and mount the mold in a supporting structure, such as

TIP: FOR A SUPER-SMOOTH FINISH, APPLY A VERY THIN LAYER OF GLAZING AND SPOT PUTTY WITH YOUR PALETTE KNIFE.

TIP: MIX ONLY THE AMOUNT OF RESIN AND HARDENER YOU NEED FOR THE JOB.

1

Larry Cotton and Phil Bowie

2

3

5

a box. Invert the mold, and fill it with mixed Bondo. (The extrusion-art syringe, mentioned below, can help fill small cavities.) Let cure, peel away the mold, and finish as described for the custom tool grip to duplicate the original. You'll probably have some small voids to fill with Bondo and/or glazing and spot putty. Our candle holder was brass colored, so we sprayed the original and the duplicate with brass paint.

3. Extruded art (cylindrical)

Modify a 20ml plastic, needleless syringe by drilling its outlet hole to ³⁄₃₂". Cut a PVC cylinder in half, lengthwise, place a removable wood disc in either end, and cover with wax paper. Put on latex gloves. Working quickly, mix the Bondo and stuff it into the syringe (messy!). Attach the cylinder to a slowly-rotating variable-speed drill and extrude Bondo from the modified syringe as it rotates. Thoroughly clean the syringe and tools between batches or they will be virtually unusable. After a full cure, carefully slide your masterpiece off one end. If it won't release, remove one or both discs to allow the cylinder to collapse slightly. If you plan to use it as a candle or lamp screen, first spray with heat-resistant paint, then line it with drafting film or similar translucent plastic. Limit lamp wattage to 60.

4. Extruded art (flat)

Tape a printout of one-line art and a sheet of wax paper to a smooth horizontal surface. Quickly extrude the mixed Bondo onto the wax paper. Repeat for any unfinished areas. You can create your own extruded art from scratch or just extrude the

body filler randomly to create fanciful ornaments.

When the Bondo is fully cured, carefully peel the wax paper from the art. No finishing is necessary except to spray paint both sides. Use small pieces of double-sided tape to mount your art on a contrasting background, or just hang it up.

5. Simulating plastic

Cover any small, prepared wood object with a thin layer of Bondo. To simulate molded radii, press the filler into intersections with a ¼"-diameter dowel. Finish as described for the customized tool grip.

6. Potting electronics

Bondo is ideal for potting and protecting circuits, either custom boards or ones exposed by careless handling. A short section of PVC tubing can help contain the Bondo. Fill and cure each end separately. Paint if the electronics will be exposed to the elements.

7. Other Bondo goodies

Fix toys. Modify or repair power tool housings. Make a small flashlight or a few throwies. Mold a sculpture. Fix a chair leg. Increase a pulley diameter. Add machine-screw threads to wood. Replace a lost screw-on lid.

For other creative uses for body filler — from Ironman helmets to rocket cones — search makezine.com or Google "body filler applications." Fond o' Bondo yet? ◉

For more projects and to share your comments, visit makezine.com/fond-o-bondo
Share it: **#makeprojects**

TIP: CLEAN AND SAND OR SCUFF THE SURFACE TO PREPARE IT FOR BODY FILLER — IT WILL NOT ADHERE TO SMOOTH, DIRTY OR OILY SURFACES.

CAUTION: BONDO IS FLAMMABLE — KEEP AWAY FROM HEAT, SPARKS, OPEN FLAMES, AND HOT SURFACES. WEAR PROTECTIVE GLOVES AND EYE/FACE PROTECTION. WASH THOROUGHLY AFTER HANDLING.

6

+SKILL BUILDER

WORKING WITH BONDO BODY FILLER

First-time Bondo'er? Get tips for mixing, preparing surfaces, and finishing at makezine.com/working-with-bondo

Vibration SENSORS

Detect motion and even individual footsteps with DIY sensors better than your smartphone's.

Written by Forrest M. Mims III

Matthew Billington

MANY METHODS HAVE BEEN IMPROVISED, INVENTED, AND HACKED TO SENSE SUDDEN MOVEMENTS, acceleration, and vibration. Today tiny, solid-state accelerometers are available to do these jobs, and they're embedded in many smartphones, tablets, and electronic game controllers. These miniature accelerometers are available for reasonable prices, or you can use the smartphone itself for vibration detection.

DIY vs. Solid-State Vibration Sensors

But there's no need for specialized accelerometer circuits if all your project needs is a simple vibration detector. Many DIY methods are available — and some are more sensitive than the solid-state accelerometers in smartphones.

This can be demonstrated with an Einstein Tablet educational computer (einsteinworld.com). The Einstein can store data from up to 16 sensors, including its own internal 3-axis accelerometer and photodiode. These 2 sensors allow us to directly compare a solid-state accelerometer with a DIY vibration sensor made of a light source and the Einstein's photodiode.

First, transform the Einstein into a pendulum by suspending it from a tabletop with 2" shipping tape. The photodiode (the dark square sensor in **Figure A**) should face down and the screen should face away from the table. Place an LED flashlight on the floor and point it up at the photodiode.

Select the accelerometer and photodiode options by checking them in the Einstein's launch window. Set the sample rate at 10 per second, the

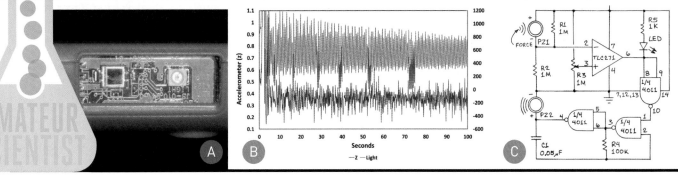

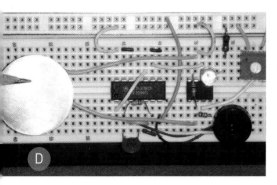

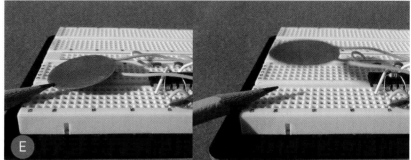

sampling duration at 50 seconds or more and the sensitivity of the photodiode at 0–600 lux. Press the Start arrow and then pull the Einstein 1" or so away from the vertical. Then release the tablet so that it swings back and forth. Experiment with the placement of the flashlight for best results.

Figure B is a chart comparing the movement response of the z-axis of the Einstein's accelerometer and its photodiode. The photodiode is plainly more sensitive to movement, and even shows a periodic wobble in the swing of the tablet. Clearly, a simple pendulum or cantilever made from a light source and a photodiode can provide a very sensitive movement and vibration detector.

Make a Piezoelectric Vibration Sensor

Here's another DIY method that's simple and doesn't need to be shielded from external light. A piezoelectric crystal or ceramic generates a voltage when it is bent or struck. A very simple vibration sensor can be made from the type of piezo ceramic disc that emits tones and sounds in watches, phones, greeting cards, and alarms.

Figure C shows a circuit that flashes an LED and emits tone bursts when piezo disc PZ1 (mine was salvaged from a greeting card) is touched or vibrated. The piezo disc is connected to the inverting input of a TLC271 or similar operational amplifier connected as a voltage comparator. A voltage divider formed by potentiometer R3 is connected to the noninverting input of the op-amp.

In operation, R3 is adjusted until the output of the op-amp switches from low to high. This switches off the tone generator formed by a 4011 quad NAND gate. A very slight mechanical shock will cause PZ1 to generate a voltage that will switch the comparator output from high to low. This will flash the LED and cause the 4011 to generate a tone burst.

This circuit can be built on a solderless breadboard (Figure D) that allows for easy modifications. For example, the tone frequency

can be decreased by increasing the value of C1. The sound volume can be increased by replacing PZ2 with the input side of a standard audio output transformer having an input impedance of 1,000Ω and an output impedance of 8Ω (RadioShack 273-1380 or equivalent). Connect a small 8Ω speaker to the transformer's output. For even more volume, connect pin 4 of the 4011 and ground to the input of an external amplifier.

The sensitivity of the circuit can best be demonstrated by connecting PZ1 to the circuit with a pair of 4", 24-gauge jumper wires as shown in Figure D. Solder one end of each wire to the connection points on the backside of the piezo disc. Connect the other 2 ends of the wires to the circuit so that the piezo disc is cantilevered, suspended about 1" over the breadboard.

When PZ1 is still, adjust R3 until the LED glows and the tone generator is on. Then back off on R3 until both the LED and the tone are off. Now when you barely touch the piezo disc, the LED and tone generator should respond. Tap the piezo disc so that it bounces up and down, and the LED and tone will respond accordingly (Figure E).

PZ1 can be kept in the cantilever mode or cemented or clipped to a wall, curtain, step, car, etc. The circuit can be made much more sensitive by cementing to its upper surface a stiff metal rod with a small weight mounted on its free end. Footsteps can be detected when a piezo disc with an attached rod is mounted on or under a flat surface such as a wood floor or step.

Going Further

Sensitive pendulum and cantilever vibration sensors can be made from hardware found in almost any workshop. Suspend a weight from the end of a vertical metal rod or mount it on the end of a horizontal metal cantilever. Mount a machine screw and nut near the movable weight so the screw can be adjusted to nearly touch the weight or its rod. You now have a movement and vibration sensitive on-off switch. ◐

Time Required: 2-3 Hours
Cost: $15-$25

FORREST M. MIMS III
(forrestmims.org), an amateur scientist and Rolex Award winner, was named by *Discover* magazine as one of the "50 Best Brains in Science." His books have sold more than 7 million copies.

Materials

- » **Op-amp integrated circuit (IC), TLC271 or similar**
- » **Quad NAND gate IC, 4011 type**
- » **Capacitor, 0.05µF** C1
- » **Resistors, 1MΩ (2)** R1 and R2, brown-black-green
- » **Potentiometer or trimmer, 100kΩ** R3
- » **Resistor, 100kΩ** R4, brown-black-yellow
- » **Resistor, 1kΩ** R5, brown-black-red
- » **LED, red or green**
- » **Piezo disc, bare** from a noisy greeting card
- » **Miniature piezo speaker such** as Maker Shed #MSPT01, makershed.com
- » **Solderless breadboard and jumper wires** Maker Shed #MKKN3 and #MKSEEED3
- » **Battery, 9V**
- » **Battery connector, 9V** such as Maker Shed #MSBAT1

How would you use vibration sensors? Comment at makezine.com/vibration-sensors

Share it: #makeprojects

Hot Outdoor Projects

Terri Bonneau

Benton Calhoun

Gunther Kirsch

Backyard Climbing Wall

With a little creativity and some expert advice, putting up a home climbing wall can be a family project and a way to stay fit. Start with a frame and add a plywood face, embedded with T-nuts. You can buy holds from climbing supply stores, but you can also mold your own from sand and polyester resin. Don't forget the crash pads! makezine. com/projects/outdoor-climbing-wall

Pedal-Powered Phone Charger

With an old AC generator, a rectifier, and a voltage regulator, you can easily rig up a mobile charging station that transforms your momentum into juice for your phone. Inside a small enclosure, the rectifier converts the AC to DC, and the regulator dials it back to a mobile device-appropriate voltage. makezine.com/projects/pedal-power-phone-charger

osborncountry.com/Sue Osborn

instructables.com

Camping Silverware Holder

Great for camping trips or to carry tools, this fabric holder easily rolls up for packing. osborncountry.com/silverwareholder

Hands-Free Water Station

Use gravity to wash your hands — suspend a jug of water from a tree. instructables. com/id/Hands-Free-Water-Station

Backyard Zip Line

Why buy a dinky, ready-made kids' kit when you can make your own industrial-strength zip line that will support the heaviest of adults? With galvanized aircraft-quality cable, a two-wheel zip pulley, and a few other parts, you can tackle this high-flying tree-to-tree transporter in a weekend. makezine.com/projects/backyard-zip-line

The days are long and you've got more time to work and play outside. Here are 10 of our favorite builds to liven up your summer.

William Abernathy

Brad Huffman

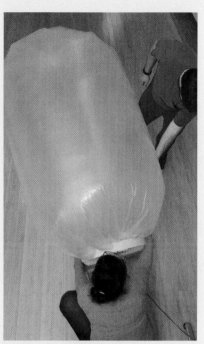

Gregory Hayes

Wood Gas Camp Stove

This elegantly simple gasifier design is called a TLUD stove (for top-lit updraft), or inverted downdraft stove. Built around a 1-quart paint can, it boils enough water for a small pot of tea or bowl of noodles, using scrap wood as fuel. makezine.com/projects/wood-gas-camp-stove

DIY Baseball Tees

Batting tees are a great tool for hitting practice. Make your own adjustable, durable tees out of PVC, dishwasher hose, plywood, and floor flanges for half the price you'd pay in the store. makezine.com/projects/diy-baseball-tees

$4 Hot Air Balloon

Fashion a balloon out of plastic drop cloths, Scotch tape, and coat hangers — and float it with an improvised burner. The envelope encloses roughly 230 cubic feet, weighs 15oz, and can lift another 15oz in payload when thoroughly heated. Unladen, these balloons have lots of extra lift for a rapid climb and a long flight. makezine.com/projects/4-hot-air-balloon

Ben Krasnow

iStockphoto.com/SarahPage

Zachery Brumberger

Astronaut Ice Cream

At very low temperature and pressure, the ice crystals in the dessert convert directly to vapor without melting into water, leaving behind a sweet, weirdly crunchy treat. Build a freeze-drying rig using a vacuum pump and a cold-trap made from copper pipe and an insulated flask, and you can make the famous snack for your next backpacking trip. makezine.com/projects/astronaut-ice-cream

Regulation Cornhole Set

This corn-bag toss game is safer than horseshoes, and it's an easy woodworking project for the whole family. All you need are two platforms and eight bags, but the American Cornhole Association (yep!) has strict regulations for dimensions, so follow their guidelines (playcornhole.org/rules.shtml) to keep your set official. instructables.com/howto/cornhole/ and makezine.com/go/diy-cornhole

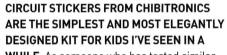

Gunther Kirsch

Circuit Stickers

Just peel and stick LEDs, sensors, and even microcontrollers, to make instant circuits.

Written by Paloma Fautley

PALOMA FAUTLEY
is an engineering intern at *Make:* magazine. She is pursuing a degree in robotics engineering and has a range of interests, from baking to pyrotechnics.

You will need:

» **Circuit Stickers Starter Kit or Deluxe Kit** NEW! Maker Shed item #MKCB01 or MKCB02, makershed.com
» **Scissors, paper, and pen**

CIRCUIT STICKERS FROM CHIBITRONICS ARE THE SIMPLEST AND MOST ELEGANTLY DESIGNED KIT FOR KIDS I'VE SEEN IN A WHILE. As someone who has tested similar kits (and has had experience with circuitry in general), I can say that this kit is worthwhile.

The included Circuit Sticker Sketchbook is a quaint yet innovative way to walk you through the learning process. The instructions are an experience in themselves: you start off with a simple circuit of an LED and a battery, and you end up with the ability to use multiple components, including sound and light sensors and even a microcontroller sticker! If you're looking for a fun and easy way to step into circuit building, this is definitely the way to go.

I put together this fun and simple array of LEDs using basic circuitry and a little creativity. All you need is copper tape, LED stickers, and a 3V coin cell battery from a Chibitronics kit, plus paper, scissors, and a pen.

1. Sketch your circuit.

After making some easy sample circuits in the Sketchbook, I sketched out a basic wiring diagram for 4 LEDs, and then copied that 6 times in an array.

2. Stick your stickers.

I placed the stickers and battery on my base layer and connected them with the copper tape. Then I added a top layer to "close the switch" — to connect the negative side of the circuit to the negative side of the battery.

3. Embellish.

I added a paper layer in between to reduce the risk of shorting the battery, and drew some designs on it for fun.

4. Activate!

Press the top layer so that the contacts are connected, and you'll see the design come to life. ◉

See more photos and share your Circuit Sticker projects at makezine.com/projects/circuit-stickers
Share it: *#makeprojects*

PROJECTS

Godzilla Detector

Written by John Iovine

Retrofit a classic Cold-War Geiger counter with new digital guts.

WHETHER IT'S THE "FUKUSHIMA PLUME" AND GIANT MONSTERS ON YOUR MIND, or you're pioneering thorium reactors in your backyard, the classic Civil Defense CDV-715 Geiger counter has a perfect retro-style case to house a modern, sensitive digital Geiger counter.

In the 1960s, at the height of the Cold War, more than half a million CDV-715 ion chamber radiological instruments were manufactured (Figure 1). In its day the CDV-715 could be found in government fallout shelters across the United States. When FEMA decommissioned the CDV-715, the instruments made their way onto the surplus market, where they're available cheap. Unfortunately, this survey instrument only detects high levels of gamma radiation that would be encountered post-nuclear attack or incident, so it's not sensitive enough for most radioactive detection work.

You can easily fix that by swapping the counter's old electronics for a new digital Geiger counter circuit and LCD Analog-Digital Meter (Figure 2a). The top line displays Counts Per Second (CPS), alternating with Approximate Radiation Level in either Imperial measurements (mR/hr) or metric (mSv/hr). The bottom line is a power meter that provides a quick visual indication of the current CPS reading (Figure 2b).

In *Make:* Volume 29, I showed how to build a Geiger counter circuit that easily fits this application. (Learn how to build it at makezine.com/projects/geiger-counter, then come back to this project for retrofitting details.) This circuit lends itself to a number of Geiger-Müller tubes available on the market (Figure 3) and can power any GM tube that requires either 400 or 500VDC. It's also compatible with the Radiation Network (radiationnetwork.com), so you can share your readings with others worldwide — in the event of global radioactive lizard outbreaks.

Optionally, paint your retro digital Geiger counter and you're ready to flip the switch and detect some particle flux! ⊘

Time Required:
1-4 Hours
Cost:
$100-$300

JOHN IOVINE is a science and electronics tinkerer and author who owns and operates Images SI Inc., a small science company. He resides in Staten Island, N.Y.

1

2a

mR 02.04

2b

3

See how to build the digital Geiger counter circuit at makezine.com/projects/geiger-counter then do your CDV-715 retrofit at makezine.com/projects/godzilla-detector

Share it: *#makeprojects*

Photo: Gunther Kirsch, Artwork: Paloma Faultly

Sure-Fire Projects for
Young Makers

BrushBot Habitats
Written by Samantha Matalone Cook

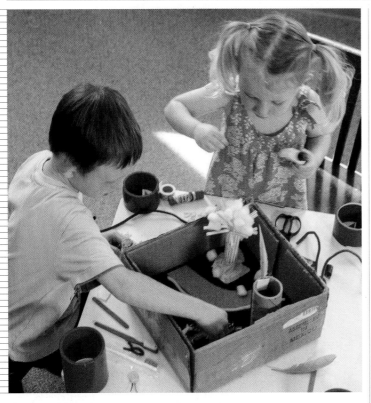

FOOLPROOF AND KIDS ARE NOT WORDS I USUALLY PUT TOGETHER. But out of the unpredictable process of working with kids come some of the most incredible ideas. My criteria, then, for a sure-fire project are based on the values we promote at Curiosity Hacked. Does it allow a child to explore a new concept or skill, with the flexibility to make it their own? Does it promote design thinking, innovation, creativity, and sustainability? Does it illustrate a level of understanding about technology in our world?

BrushBot Habitats is a simple project that's successful every time we offer it. It's accessible, affordable, and can be changed to suit the needs of any age group. By success, I mean kids (and adults!) are truly engaged in the process by which they create unique and innovative designs.

BrushBots or BristleBots are a fun project for any age. But the bot's not the focus of this project. The Habitat is. We like to bring in all kinds of recycled and household materials for this project: paper towel tubes, cardboard, duct tape, straws, Popsicle sticks, plastic bottles. The challenge is to create a Habitat for the bot that the child envisions.

Younger kids tend to build battle rings and mazes; older kids have produced beautiful labyrinths, multilevel structures, castles with working drawbridges, and even a zip line!

We love this project because it includes all the values I listed above, plus it's comfortable and fun, especially for families new to making. There is no failure, because there's no preconceived idea of what a Habitat should look like. The learner controls the learning. For me, that's as sure-fire as it gets.

Props to Evil Mad Scientist Labs, who got the whole bot world buzzing with their toothbrush BristleBot. ◗

Got a sure-fire project for little ones? Tell us at makezine.com/sure-fire
Share it: #makeprojects

Time Required:
1 Hour
Cost:
$0-$5

You will need:
» **Recycled/household materials** such as paper towel tubes, cardboard, duct tape, straws, popsicle sticks, plastic bottles
» **Scissors**
» **Tape and glue**

SAMANTHA MATALONE COOK
is the founder and executive director of Curiosity Hacked, a national nonprofit based in Oakland, California, that empowers kids to learn new skills and STEAM concepts. She also writes for GeekMom.

FREE POSTER

Make:'s Michelle Hlubinka drew this fantastic poster about what "Makers Believe" — download it at makezine.com/sure-fire for free, and slap it on the wall for all to see!

BRUSHBOTS PARTY PACK

In just a few steps, you'll turn toothbrush heads, pager motors, and coin-cell batteries into spinning, speeding bots. The bristles act as hundreds of miniature legs that propel the BrushBots, buzzing and bumping, on their way. Each kit makes 12 wacky BrushBots. Maker Shed item #MSBBRP, $35 at makershed.com. You can also build BristleBots from scratch at makezine.com/bristlebot, or use similar small robots like HexBugs.

Party Popper Toy Cannon

Written by Paul Rawlinson ■ Illustrations by Julie West

1

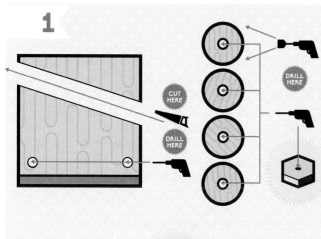

2

3

MOST LITTLE BOYS PLAY WAR, BUT YOU CAN'T GET YOUR HANDS ON THE REALLY COOL TOYS UNTIL YOU'RE AN ADULT. I wanted to bridge that gap a little by making a working toy cannon. This was a quick model made with very little planning, but by taking your time on the details, you could easily make a better version.

1. Drill. For the wheels, drill 4 cores (27mm) from 5mm wood using the hole saw, then drill 7mm holes in the center of each. » Drill two 7mm holes through the width of the wood block, in the bottom front and rear, to accept axles. » Drill a 2mm hole through the compression cap.

2. Assemble the cannon. Insert the axle dowels and use a blob of wood glue to attach each wheel permanently. » Attach the copper pipe to the top of the block using the saddle clips and screws, leaving a slight overhang on both sides of the cart.

3. Load and fire! Disassemble 5 party poppers and tie together the 5 mini explosives. Feed one string through the hole in the compression cap. » Using the pair of adjustable wrenches, tighten on the compression cap so that the "olive" ring binds, then loosen it slightly so that later you can remove and retighten it by hand. » Using the third dowel, ram a cotton ball or two down the barrel of the cannon, so they sit over the explosives. Lastly, add the ammo (I used a lid from a soy sauce bottle) and you're ready! Pull the string to fire.

You can easily make your own adjustments to this cannon design to make all different types and styles. ◕

Visit makezine.com/projects/toycannon for step-by-step photos, troubleshooting tips, and video of the cannon in action.

Share it: #makeprojects

PAUL RAWLINSON makes random projects and shares the results on his site, go-repairs.blogspot.co.uk and YouTube channel, youtube.com/user/gorepairs/.

You will need:
» **Wood block, 77mm long × 43mm wide, with the top chopped at a 15° angle**
» **Wood circles, 27mm diameter × 5mm thick (4)**
» **Wood dowels, 6mm diameter × 300mm long (3)**
» **Copper pipe, 15mm diameter × 110mm long**
» **Pipe fitting, compression cap, brass, 15mm**
» **Copper pipe clips, 15mm (2) aka saddle clips**
» **Wood screws, small (4)**
» **Cotton balls**
» **"Party popper" confetti shooters (5)**
» **Bottle lid, plastic, less than 15mm diameter**
» **Wood glue**
» **Drill**
» **Drill bit, hole saw, 27mm**
» **Drill bit, wood, 7mm**
» **Drill bit, metal, 2mm**
» **Adjustable wrenches (2)**

WARNING: TAKE ALL NECESSARY PRECAUTIONS AND WEAR SAFETY EQUIPMENT DURING THIS BUILD. HANDLE PARTY POPPERS CAREFULLY, AS THEY DO CONTAIN EXPLOSIVES, AND NEVER FIRE AT ANYONE.

makezine.com/projects/40

Toy Inventor's Notebook

SUPER-CHEAP ELECTRONIC DICE CHALLENGE

Invented and drawn by Bob Knetzger

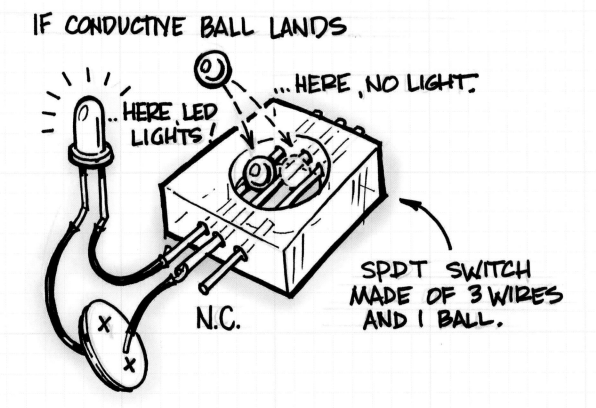

IF CONDUCTIVE BALL LANDS

... HERE, LED LIGHTS!

... HERE, NO LIGHT.

N.C.

SPDT SWITCH MADE OF 3 WIRES AND 1 BALL.

SUPPOSE YOU WANTED TO BUILD ELECTRONIC DICE FOR A BOARD GAME. Sure, you could use discrete components to build a clock circuit into a decade counter and BCD to 7-segment decoder, etc. Or you could write some random number generating code for an Arduino and use LEDs. That's obvious and has been done before. But professional toy inventors have to be crazy clever and get the same effect, but for an insanely low, dirt-cheap cost. Can you do it?

Here's one approach that costs next to nothing: It's just LEDs wired up with some cleverly designed SPDT switches. Each switch is made of three parallel wires and a metal ball in a cage. When you shake the cage, the ball randomly lands on either one pair of wires or the other pair. Only one pair of wires completes the circuit, lighting the LED.

To make an electronic die, I'd wire up 4 LEDs to one switch, 2 LEDs to the next switch, and a single LED to the last switch (**Figure 1**). Shake them all together and you'll get a random number of LEDs to light up, from 0 to 7. For games that need a number from 1 to 6, just "roll" again if you get 0 or 7 lit LEDs.

Your challenge: Can you rewire the switches so that you'll only get numbers 1 through 6 — so that "0" and "7" never appear? Here's a blank for you to draw your wires (**Figure 2**). (Hint: the new version may not be a "fair" die, but its average roll yield will be the same as a real die.) ●

Go to makezine.com/electronic-dice for the solution!
Share it: *#makeprojects*

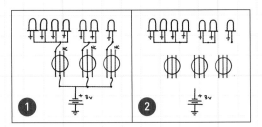

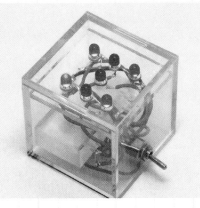

Byrnes Model Machines Table Saw

$450 : byrnesmodelmachines.com

The high-quality table saw has a 4" blade, a fence that locks absolutely parallel, an adaptable miter gauge, and a built-in micrometer stop. This beautiful, handcrafted machine is built by Jim Byrnes, a model ship builder, and his small crew of craftsmen in Florida, entirely from milled aluminum components.

At my company, Beatty Robotics, we find that builder-grade power tools are often too large and crude for the finer work we do. We like small, precision tools that purr rather than roar, but be warned: With a maximum cut width of 3.865" (6" on custom order), this saw is only for your smallest work. With the right blade, the saw can cut wood, plastic, aluminum, and other nonferrous materials.

Although a little pricey, the Byrnes is the best of the best among small high-precision table saws. —*Robert Beatty*

Robert Beatty

SMART SIZZORS
$25 : anysharp.com

Smart Sizzors are do-it-all scissors that are equally functional in the home, kitchen, or workshop. Their curved, hardened steel blades are beasts that can easily cut through a wide range of soft fabrication materials, such as foam, fabric, or flexible tubing. The handles are comfortable and appropriately grippy, and there's even a pivot tension adjustment that allows for tightening or loosening up to suit your preference. Multipurpose grooves and cutters are built inside the handles and are perfect for everything from stripping wires to smashing garlic. After having these in my drawer for a couple of weeks, they've become my go-to snips and they haven't let me down yet. —*Goli Mohammadi*

HARBOR FREIGHT COMBINATION SANDER
$250 : harborfreight.com

This combination belt and disk sander is one of those shop tools that I just cannot live without. With the right sandpaper, it's great for quickly deburring most materials, including wood, plastic, and even metal. The belt and disk offer fine control with quick material removal, allowing you to contour, smoothly bevel, and radius almost anything. With a simple jig you can even make perfect circles with it. I've used one for more than 10 years and have never had any problems, although it could benefit from a few tweaks and user-made upgrades.

—*Dan Spangler*

Gunther Kirsch

Dremel Fortiflex Flex-Shaft Tool

$239 : dremel.com

There are everyday rotary tools, and then there's the Fortiflex, a heavy-duty flex-shaft machine. In addition to its more powerful motor, Fortiflex's bit speed is controlled using a foot pedal that allows for instant changes depending on what the project calls for.

Setup was easy, and the kit came with a few choice bits, including a tungsten carbide cutter that was impressive enough to turn heads on its own.

Using the Fortiflex alongside an ordinary corded Dremel is like upgrading to a Cadillac from a Schwinn. I used both to carve out a precise pattern in oak, and the Fortiflex felt better in every single way. The handpiece is solid and gives you far more control with fine work (the kind these tools excel at) than your average rotary tool. It feels stronger and lighter, as if you've not only been granted superpowers but also the instinct to use them.

—Sam Freeman

COROPLAST CORRUGATED PLASTIC SHEETING MATERIAL

$ varies : www.coroplast.com

Corrugated Plastic, also known by the Coroplast® trade name, is typically used in low-cost, lightweight, or temporary sign printing applications. It has a construction similar to corrugated cardboard, but is instead made from polypropylene plastic, which is more weather-resistant.

I especially like using this material for LED lighting projects because it is lightweight and very easy to work with. There are many ways to cut Coroplast — I often use a carpet cutter — and you can drill holes through it as if it was a sturdier material.

Inexpensive, Coroplast can be found in a few sizes at most big-box hardware stores, and sign shops and plastic dealers often carry it in different colors and thicknesses. *—Tyler Winegarner*

TOOLS

WAGO LEVER-NUTS

Price varies, ~$0.50+ each : wago.us

The beauty of Lever-Nuts is that they're a quick, easy, and tool-free means of creating temporary, long-term, or even permanent electrical connections. I use the 3-conductor connectors most often, but the 2- and 5-port ones are also quite useful.

Lever-Nuts can be used on stranded and solid wires as thin as 28 AWG and as thick as 12 AWG, and are rated up to 600V and 20A. You can use them in place of crimp-on splices, screw terminals, or other such wiring fixtures.

To use Lever-Nuts, all you have to do is strip about 10mm of insulation off your wire. You don't even need to hunt down a ruler to do so, as each Lever-Nut has a stripping guide built-in. Also built-in are access holes perfectly sized for multimeter probes.

— *Stuart Deutsch*

XURON WICKGUN DESOLDERING BRAID DISPENSER

$32 : xuron.com

Once a joint is heated, solder braids can wick up molten solder for removal, often more precisely than suction-based systems. The WickGun's braid dispenser is convenient, but it's really the built-in cutter that's the great time saver. The ability to expose and cut the braid with one hand means no more wasted time reaching for snips, cutters, or blades.

The dispenser is easy to load, and the replaceable cartridges are packed with high-quality, fine-braided wick. Desoldering with the WickGun went faster than with my usual wick, and (naturally) produced cleaner results than my solder sucker. — *SF*

FADECANDY

$25 : adafruit.com

Built with red, green, and blue channels, and independently addressable controllers, WS2812 LEDs are colorful and fun devices to build with. It's a cinch to work with a few of these LEDs, but larger projects that involve matrices or many rows of strips can be challenging to get things looking exactly as planned. That's where Fadecandy comes in — it's a USB-based controller that helps ease programming so you can focus more on creative aspects.

Fadecandy can also make your LED pixel projects look better through interpolation, dithering, and higher resolution colors. Each Fadecandy can support as many as 512 WS2812 LEDs, in 8 strings of 64, and you can use multiple controller boards for larger projects. It can be run from desktop computers, laptops, and even Raspberry Pis. — *SD*

NEW MAKER TECH

PIXY CAMERA

$69 : charmedlabs.com

Pixy is a video-based vision sensor that can handle object recognition and tracking, face detection, and color filtering. In addition to being a very capable image processor, Pixy is easy to use and integrate with Arduino boards and other microcontrollers.

Once Pixy identifies an object, it can report on it through any of several data communication interfaces, including USB, I2C, SPI, UART serial, digital, and analog outputs. It can then pass on information about things like object size and location, and it does this 50 times a second.

Best of all, at $69, Pixy is an affordable way to get started with vision sensors. — *SD*

GET BUILDING:
ROBOTICS KITS

 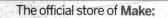

NEW MAKER TECH

JETSON TK1

$192 : developer.nvidia.com/jetson-tk1

If you're familiar with Nvidia, it's likely you'll first think of their powerful graphics processors that are built for hardcore computer gaming rigs. However, the company also produces graphics and computer vision hardware for medical, automotive, and industrial applications. Nvidia is now interested in seeing what makers can do with their technology.

Of interest to makers is Nvidia's recently released Jetson TK1 Development Kit, which is based on the Tegra family of chips found in many modern mobile devices. The board has a Tegra K1 system-on-chip, which includes a GPU with 192 CUDA cores and a quad-core ARM Cortex A15 CPU. While it's too early to tell, this just might end up being the go-to Linux board for demanding graphics or computer vision-based projects.

— Matt Richardson

ARDUINO ZERO

$TBD : arduino.cc

Arduino's new Zero microcontroller board might look similar to their Uno and Leonardo boards, but it packs some big differences under the hood. Powered by a 32-bit ARM Cortex M0+ processor, the new board is significantly faster and much more capable than Arduino's 8-bit boards. It also comes with 256KB of flash memory and 32KB of SRAM, a big increase over what's currently available.

All of the Zero board's digital pins, except the Rx/Tx pins, can be used as PWM pins. Also, its 6 analog input pins are passed through a 12-bit ADC — instead of a 10-bit ADC — giving it significantly better analog resolution.

Like the Arduino Due — the first Arduino microcontroller board to be based on an ARM core — the Zero runs at 3.3V, and so it can only work with 3.3V-compatible shields.

The Zero is also the first Arduino board to support Atmel's Embedded Debugger (EDBG), which provides a full debug interface without the need for additional hardware.

—Alasdair Allan

LITTLEBITS ARDUINO MODULE

$36 (module), $89 (starter pack) : littlebits.cc

The littleBits platform of modular electronics just became programmable with their new Arduino Module, released at Maker Faire Bay Area 2014. An official "Arduino at Heart" product, the module is compatible with other bits in the littleBits collection and is programmed with Arduino code and the Arduino development environment.

The board has the typical types of inputs and outputs you'd find on an Arduino Leonardo. Two of the outputs can be switched between a pulse-width modulation mode and an analog voltage mode. Serial connections are broken out so multiple Arduino modules can communicate together. There are also solder pads, allowing access to more IO pins for the advanced maker. Whether you're playing or prototyping, the new module brings the wonderful worlds of Arduino and littleBits together in an empowering way.

—MR

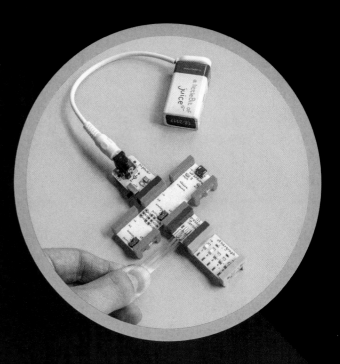

BOOKS

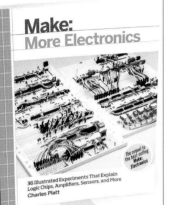

MAKE: MORE ELECTRONICS
By Charles Platt
$35 : Maker Media

I thought the 36 experiments in Charles Platt's *Make: Electronics* were plenty to jumpstart my electronics skills, but apparently I was wrong. A quick skim of the next 36 experiments found in the just-released sequel, *Make: More Electronics,* has shown me that I've only just skimmed the surface of what I will be capable of doing in my little workshop when I finish the book. More projects, more "learning by discovery" — aka burning out components and making mistakes — and absolutely more from the best electronics tutor on the planet. These are the two books that will give you the electronics skills to do amazing things.

—*James Floyd Kelly*

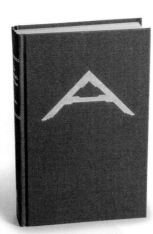

THE ANARCHIST'S TOOL CHEST
By Christopher Schwarz
$37 (hardbound) : Lost Art Press

Woodworking is a rewarding craft and hobby to pursue, but it can also be confusing and costly for beginners. Ask a seasoned woodworker about which essential tools you will need, and they will often rattle off a list of tools that will make your head spin.

The Anarchist's Tool Chest is not your average beginner's book, and its author is not your average seasoned woodworker. In this book, Schwarz will tell you all about the hand tools a woodworker needs, as well as those you don't, and more importantly he tells you why. He takes you on a tour through the traditional woodworking shop and finishes the book by showing you how to build a tool chest.

Schwarz's writing style is unlike what you'll find in any other woodworking reference. He speaks to you in a friendly and frank nature. It's as if this book is his diary or a long correspondence to a personal friend.

While I don't always agree with Schwarz's approach, I feel this book should be standard reading for anyone who hopes to one day call themselves a woodworker.

—*Stuart Deutsch*

MANUFACTURING PROCESSES FOR DESIGN PROFESSIONALS
By Rob Thompson
$95 : Thames & Hudson

This beautifully photographed and organized book is part coffee-table book, part serious encyclopedic reference of manufacturing processes. Complete with diagrams and case studies, it is a comprehensive view of the industrial stack that makes modern product manufacturing possible.

Whenever I reach for the book to look up something specific, I lose myself in the pages, as there's always more to learn.

Amateur makers with commercial aspirations could quickly learn enough to speak competently with contract manufacturers, and — perhaps more importantly — they will learn and better understand the breadth of what can be done.

—*Robert Cook*

RASPBERRY PI COMPUTE MODULE
$30 (per 100) : raspberrypi.org

If you want to incorporate a Raspberry Pi more tightly into your products or projects, the new Compute Module might just be what you're looking for. Jammed into a board the size of a stick of RAM, the Compute Module packs in much of the core Raspberry Pi features and adds things like onboard flash storage.

Since the Compute Module borrows its form factor from a RAM module, it makes designing a printed circuit board with the brains of a Raspberry Pi much easier. Now your gnarly prototype for a DIY cell phone could become a sleek smartphone!

—*MR*

eSUN易生 3D FILAMENT

SGS

www.esun3d.net en.esunchina.net

ENVIRONMENT-FRIENDLY   **S**TEADY QUALITY
FUNCTIONAL DIVERSITY   ECO**N**OMICAL PRICE

PLA	NYLON
ABS	CONDUCTIVE
PVA	WOOD
HIPS	FLEXIBLE
PC	

Accept Customized

Esun:bright@brightcn.net +86-755-26031978
Esun distributor in FL: sales@knkusa.com 1 407-701-4830
Esun distributor in CA: sales@toybuilderlabs.com +1 626 808 4010 x.700

MAKE $5,000
BY CREATING AN ACCESSORY FOR SPHERO!

sphero

Learn more at:
gosphero.com/make5000
Deadline for entries is August 15, 2014

WORLD'S MOST VERSATILE
CIRCUIT
BOARD HOLDERS

Model 324

Our Circuit Board Holders add versatility & precision to your DIY electronics project. Solder, assemble & organize with ease.

VISIT US ON

MONTHLY CONTEST

Visit us on Facebook® to post a photo of your creative PanaVise project for a chance to win a PanaVise prize package.

Model 201

PANAVISE®
Innovative Holding Solutions

7540 Colbert Drive • Reno • Nevada 89511 | (800) 759-7535 | www.PanaVise.com

INTRODUCING...
DREMEL MICRO
BRILLIANTLY POWERFUL

Speed Dial

8V MAX Lithium-Ion

LED Light

DREMEL MICRO

Speed Indicator

Visit Dremel.com to learn more

My Thermoelectrically Cooled Pillow

Written by Victor Konshin

VICTOR KONSHIN
is an engineer, inventor, author, serial entrepreneur, and gadget freak living in Williamsville, New York.

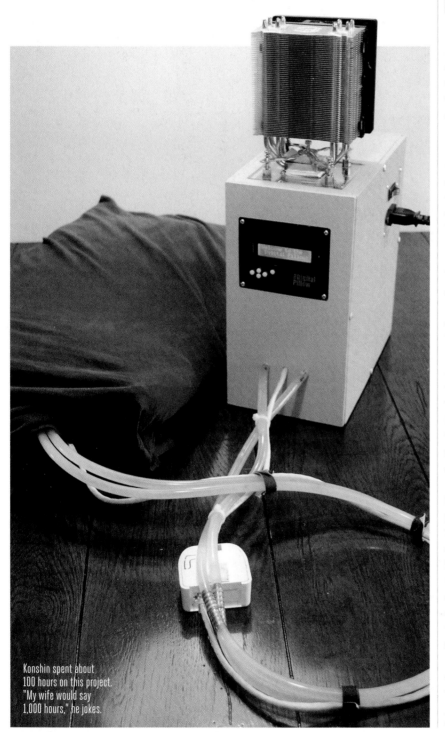

Konshin spent about 100 hours on this project. "My wife would say 1,000 hours," he jokes.

DO YOU HATE A HOT PILLOW? ARE YOU CONSTANTLY TURNING YOUR PILLOW OVER, ALL NIGHT LONG? Me too, so I created the Digital Pillow, the world's first microprocessor controlled, water-cooled pillow — and it works.

I started with a simple proof-of-concept prototype that consisted of two CPU coolers: a simple air-cooled heatsink and a water heat exchanger. I placed a solid-state, semiconductor heat pump called a Peltier junction between the two. I connected a small water pump and ran a coil of tubing through a pillow.

This worked well but had some problems. The pillow was warm at first because the padding insulates, but by morning it was too cold. I realized the only way to solve these problems was to add a microcontroller and redesign the "human interface" — the pillow itself.

The design I ended up with uses an Arduino Micro, 10 temperature sensors, two ultraquiet fans, a speed-controlled water pump, a water flow sensor and an LCD display with keypad. I also upgraded to a 231-watt Peltier junction that generates 788 BTU of cooling power and a 20-amp power supply to power it all. Overengineering? What's that?

For the pillow, I used a large rugged water bladder that I stitched to the top of a standard polyfill pillow and attached hose fittings to the cap. The pillow contains six temperature sensors that send the pillow temperature back to the Arduino, which then regulates the Peltier junction power to maintain a constant, comfortable temperature. Other temperature sensors monitor the junction and power supply temperatures and adjust the fan and pump speeds to the minimum settings needed to keep the system running cool. After an initial cool-down cycle that lasts about six minutes, the Digital Pillow runs almost silently. ⊘

+ For more info on this project, check out thedigitalpillow.com.

Victor Konshin